POMPEII A·D 79

Volume II

POMPEII A·D 79

Treasures from the National Archaeological Museum, Naples,
with contributions from the Pompeii Antiquarium
and the Museum of Fine Arts, Boston

Essay and Catalogue by
JOHN WARD-PERKINS AND AMANDA CLARIDGE
with additions by the Department of Classical Art,
Museum of Fine Arts, Boston

Museum of Fine Arts, Boston

The Art Institute of Chicago

Dallas Museum of Fine Arts

American Museum of Natural History

Made possible by grants from
The National Endowment for the Humanities
and Xerox Corporation

Library of Congress catalog card no. 78-54015

ISBN 0-8-846-124-8

Typeset by Dumar Typesetting, Dayton, Ohio

Printed in U.S.A.
by Case-Hoyt, Rochester, New York

Designed by Carl Zahn

Photograph Credits:

Photographs for nos. 30, 31, 34-36, 42, 43, 45,
46, 48, 49, 51, 53, 54, 73, 93, 95, 96, 112a,b,
132, 134, 142, 157, 158, 160, 163, 169, 172,
181, 203, 205, 212, 228, 237, 258, 259, 263,
269, 271-274, 287a, 298, 324, 326 were supplied by Giuseppe Musco on behalf of the Soprintendenza Archeologica delle Province di Napoli
e Caserta.

Photographs of the objects lent by the Metropolitan Museum of Art and the Museum of Fine
Arts, Boston, were supplied by the museum
concerned.

All other photographs by Eric de Maré, maps
and diagrams by Michael Robinson except those
listed below.

Pages 33 (both), 39 (below), Nos. 185, 243,
260-262, 264, 265, 267, 268, Amanda Claridge

Pages 96 (center row), 100 (top left, bottom
right), 103 (bottom), Nos. 115, 116, Deutsches
Archäologisches Institut, Rome

Map of Pompeii pages 46 and 47, Hans Eschebach

Pages 36, 39 (top), 82 (top), 96 (bottom row),
100 (far right, top, and left center), No. 20, Foto
Alinari, Rome

Plan for No. 90, Sheila Gibson

Pages 96 (center row), 100 (middle of top row),
Nos. 27, 108, 193, 236, 277, 279, 280, 282-287,
327, Edgar Hyman and Peter Chorley

No. 38 (profile), Alan Irvine

Sources of plans for page 53, Dr. Ann Laidlaw

Nos. 11, 12, Museo della Civiltà Romana

Pages 60, 63, 82, 90, 105-108, Nos. 3-5,
7-10, 29, 33, 39, 55, 58, 68, 80-84, 86, 89, 92,
106, 109, 114, 129, 137, 147, 152, 154, 162,
177, 178, 180, 190-192, 196, 197, 199, 200,
206, 219, 241, 244-247, 253, 276, 293-295,
311, 312, 325, Museo Nazionale Archeologico,
Naples

Page 51, Pubbli Aerfoto, Milan

Cover, title page, pages 6, 7, 14, 15, 17, 18, 19,
20, 21, 22, 23, 25, 26 (left), 27, 65, 66, 67, 68,
69, 70, 71, 72-73, 74, 75, 76, 77, 80, Strüwing
Reklamefoto, Birkerod, Denmark

Reconstruction drawing for No. 87, Florence
Wolsky

Acknowledgments:

The introductory essays in volume I of this
catalogue as well as the majority of the
entries in volume II were reprinted from the
British edition of *Pompeii* A.D. 79. The
authors, John Ward-Perkins and Amanda
Claridge, have kindly consented to the
"conversion" in their text from British to
American usage in spelling and punctuation.
References to objects shown in London but
not in this exhibition have been omitted.
The Soprintendenza Archeologica delle
Province di Napoli e Caserta has granted
the loan of several objects almost identical
to the pieces withdrawn, and for these sub-
stitutions the entries of Mr. Ward-Perkins
and Miss Claridge have been modified as
necessary. The catalogue was edited by
Margaret Jupe (volume II) and Judy Spear
(volume I). We thank Peter Saabor, of
Carlton Cleve Limited, London, for facili-
tating contact between authors and editors
and for arranging the loans of the exhibition material belonging to Imperial
Tobacco Limited.

Since the London exhibition, the Soprintendenza Archeologica has generously
granted a number of important new loans
for the showings of "Pompeii A.D. 79" in
Denmark and the United States. Entries for
these objects, Nos. 30, 31, 33-36, 42, 43,
45, 46, 48, 49, 51, 53-55, 58, 73, 87, 89,
95, 96, 112a,b, 117-128, 132, 134, 142,
157, 158, 169, 172, 181, 203, 206, 212,
228, 237, 253, 258, 259, 263, 271-274,
287a, 293-295, 298, 311, 312, 324-326,
were written by members of the Department of Classical Art, Ariel Herrmann,
John Herrmann, Cornelius Vermeule, and
Florence Wolsky. Mary Comstock had a
vital role as organizer of our efforts and as
editor and researcher. In preparing the
entries, we were greatly aided by Hans
Eric Wallin of the Louisiana Museum,
Humlebaek, Denmark, who placed at our
disposal the photographs and descriptions
provided him by the Soprintendenza Archeologica. We are grateful to Mr. Wallin and
to Margaret MacLeod of the WGBH
Educational Foundation, Boston, for
arranging for several new color photographs. We also wish to thank Dr. Maria
Giuseppina Cerulli-Irelli, Director of
Excavations, Pompeii, Dr. Mariarosaria
Borriello d'Ambrosio, and Giuseppe Tucci
of the Naples Museum for advice and for
research on provenances. Catherine
Springer kindly provided information for
the cataloguing and display of the frescoes
from the Metropolitan Museum of Art.

A special word of appreciation should go
to the conservators and handlers responsible for the condition and safety of the
objects: the laboratory of the Soprintendenza Archeologica, directed by Dr. Ciro
Piccioli, and Dr. Ermanno de Marinis,
responsible for packing and for shipping
the objects to the United States; the
Research Laboratory of the Museum of
Fine Arts, Boston, which not only super-
vised the handling of the American material
but also undertook conservation of the
Boston frescoes to prepare them for display;
and the conservators of the Metropolitan Museum of Art. Thanks are also
due to the designers of the exhibition, Tom
Wong and Judith Downes, whose mount-
ings will travel to the participating
museums. The advice and skills of these
technicians were necessary preconditions
for the new loans as well as for the con-
tinuance of the exhibition.

Finally, we acknowledge with gratitude
the collaboration of the many museum col-
leagues who gave their time and talents to
this project; we are especially indebted to
Linda Thomas, registrar, Lisa Simon,
grants coordinator, and the staff of the
Design Department.

JOHN HERRMANN
Exhibition Coordinator
Department of Classical Art

CONTENTS
Volume II

1 (color plate, vol. I, title page)
Pair of villa landscapes
Width 53 cm, height 22 cm
Naples Museum, inv. 9406
From Pompeii

Two separate views of villa façades probably from the lateral panels of a Third Style scheme (see illustration p. 96), now mounted as a pair. The left-hand view shows a straight porticoed façade upraised on a platform with a tall columnar central porch; in front of the portico is a garden with a large axial enclosure and at either end, rising from a lower level, is a double portico, of two orders, facing outward. Above and beyond the right-hand portico is the façade of a temple-like building facing inward; there may have been other buildings or trees in the damaged upper left-hand part. The right-hand view shows a central gabled porch at the junction of two gable-ended, inward-facing porticoes, enclosing on three sides a trapezoidal space concentric to which is an enclosure with posts at the angles. Above and behind rise a number of other buildings including a circular *tempietto* (*tholos*) and another colonnade. The perspective of these scenes is syntactic, and some of the detail (e.g., the half-gables of the flanking porticoes on the left-hand panel) is without parallel in surviving contemporary architecture, but it is generally accepted that such façades were a feature of the wealthy *villae marittimae*.
Peters 115f.

2 (color plate, vol. I, p. 6)
Painting of a villa beside the sea
Diameter 25 cm
Naples Museum, inv. 9511
From Stabiae

Roundel portraying the two-storied columnar façade of a *villa marittima*. The center of the façade curves inward, toward a tower-like circular feature. In front is a platform with two projecting jetties, human figures, and statues. Beyond are other buildings, trees, and a rocky crag on which are trees and what appears to be a group of statuary. The roundel and its companion pieces (Naples Museum, inv. 9408, 9409) would have occupied the centers of large panels in a Fourth Style scheme, comparable to those in the first room off the peristyle in the House of "Loreius Tiburtinus" (II, 2, 2-5; Schefold, *WP* 51).
Rostowzew, "Architekturlandschaft" 75(b); Peters 157.

I

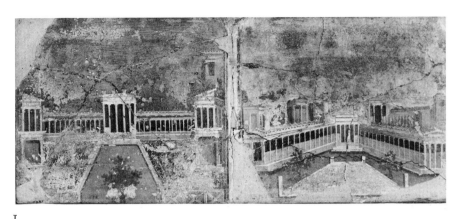

2

3
Painting of a villa beside the sea
Length 39.5 cm, height 17 cm
Naples Museum, inv. 9480
From Stabiae

The seaward frontage of an elaborate *villa marittima;* in the foreground is a platform with arches and steps down to the water, and in the background are other buildings, gardens, and a rocky eminence crowned by a temple. On the platform are sketched figures, at the bottom right-hand corner part of a boat, and behind it a statue posed on a rock.

Probably from the center of a panel in a Third Style wall, as in the *tablinum* of the House of M. Lucretius Fronto (see page 96) or possibly used like the landscapes or still lifes in the wall schemes of the courtyard of the Temple of Isis.
Rostowzew, "Architekturlandschaft" 75, no. 3; Peters 159f.

3

4
Sacro-idyllic landscape
Width 30 cm, height 26 cm
Naples Museum, inv. 9447
From Herculaneum

Highly impressionistic view of a rustic
sanctuary, a small, circular, tower-like
structure, a rocky crag, and trees. On the
left a figure is carrying a basin; on the
right another figure stoops before a herm.
In the center, in shadowy outline, is a
statue on a pedestal.

Presumably from the field of a Fourth
Style lateral panel, as in the atrium of the
House of Fabius Amandio (I, 7, 2-3).

5 (color plate, vol. I, p. 7)
Painting of a sanctuary beside the sea
Width 62 cm, height 52 cm
Naples Museum, inv. 9482
From Pompeii

Painted in light colors on a black ground,
this fragment portrays a sanctuary, set on
a rocky island or promontory, and in the
foreground two boats. The details of the
sanctuary are conventional; a central, circular shrine, or *tholos*, flanked by porticoes and a re-entrant façade wall; in front
of this, facing onto the water, is an open
platform, on which are several groups of
figures, including a woman and a dog. On
the enclosure wall is a statue, and beyond
it are trees and buildings perched on
rocks. In the left margin are traces of a
frame and part of an ornamental column.

The scene probably formed part of a
much larger panel set between columns as
on the Third Style wall, found at Pompeii
on 23 August 1758 (*Pitture di Ercolano* II,
p. 273, pl. L), which shows above, in the
background, a similar sanctuary; in the
middle is a boat and below, in the foreground, another island sanctuary and a
fisherman.

Rostowzew, "Architekturlandschaft" 52;
Peters 117f.

6
Wall painting: temple in a landscape
Width 65 cm, height 40 cm
Naples Museum, inv. 9487
From Pompeii

Sacro-idyllic landscape, probably from
the middle of one of the lateral panels of a
Fourth Style wall. It portrays a small
temple in a setting of trees. In front of the
temple two figures sacrifice at an altar;
behind it is a statue in a columnar setting.
In the distance can be seen a portico.

4

5

6

7

8

7
Seascape with boats and buildings
Width 33 cm, height 23 cm
Naples Museum, inv. 9463
From Pompeii

A small, highly impressionistic landscape,
including a central *tholos* on a rocky islet
with a jetty and two fishermen, a porticoed
façade with trees beyond it, and two
boats. The scene is viewed as if across a
palisaded fence and appears to come from
one of the complex architectural framing
members of a Fourth Style scheme, as
Nos. 144, 145.
Rostowzew, "Architekturlandschaft" 85,
note 2.

8
Landscape panel within a stucco cornice
Length 2.10 m, height 52 cm
Naples Museum, inv. 9496
From the *exedra* off the west side of the
middle peristyle of the House of the
Citharist (I, 4, 5)

A long, narrow, idealized landscape and
seascape, set within a stucco cornice of
which the left end is missing. At the left
end of the field, on a fortified rocky promontory, can be seen a small temple and, at
the foot of the slope, a large seated statue
on a tall pedestal, accompanied by the
inevitable tree. The unusual building with
three receding stories is thought to represent a *belvedere*. Beyond it and at the right
end are two rather similar buildings with
landing stages and porticoed façades enclosing gardens and other buildings, free
representations of *villae marittimae*. In
the right foreground stands a large urn on
a pedestal. This picture blends into a
single romantic landscape elements that
are derived from a variety of sources,
among them some that are derived from
the Hellenistic Nilotic landscapes and
from the sacro-idyllic repertory and
others from the contemporary architecture of the Campanian *villae marittimae*.
Rostowzew, "Architekturlandschaft" 91,
no. 4; Peters 165f.

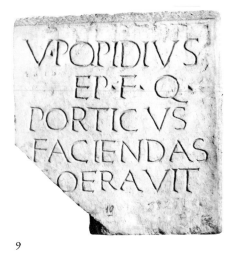

V·POPIDIVS
EP·F·Q·
PORTIC VS
FACIENDAS
OERAVIT

9

N·POPIDIVS·N·F·CELSINVS
AEDEM·ISIDIS·TERR·A·E·MOTV·CONLAPSAM
A·FVNDAMENTO·P·S·R·ESTITVIT·HVNC·DECVRIONES·OB·LIBERALITATEM
CVM·ESSET·ANNORVM·SEXS·ORDINI·SVO·GRATIS·ADLEGERVNT

10

9

Inscribed slab recording the building of the colonnade round the Forum
Limestone
Height 45.5 cm, width 44 cm
Naples Museum, inv. 3825
Found in 1814 in the Forum, near the entrance to the Basilica

V[ibius] Popidius Ep[idii] f[ilius] q[uaestor] porticus faciendas coeravit.
"Vibius Popidius, son of Epidius, quaestor, had charge of the building of this portico."

The inscription, which dates from the last period before the foundation of the Sullan colony in 80 B.C., records the construction of a portico, built of tufa, around the central open area of the Forum. This Samnite portico, which marked an important step in the monumentalization of the city center, was in process of being replaced at the time of the earthquake and the eruption. The official in charge, Vibius Popidius, was at the time a *quaestor,* one of the junior magistrates of the Samnite town. He belonged to a very prominent indigenous Pompeian family, the Popidii,

who are known to have provided at least two chief magistrates (*meddices*) of the pre-Roman period.
CIL x. 794; *ILS* 5538.

10

Inscribed slab recording the rebuilding of the Temple of Isis
Marble, recomposed from 37 pieces
Length 2.35 m, height 49.5 cm
Naples Museum, inv. 3765
Found in 1765 fallen from its position over the entrance from the street to the Temple

N[umerius] Popidius N[umerii] f[ilius] Celsinus aedem Isidis terrae motu conlapsam a fundamento p[ecunia] s[ua] restituit. Hunc decuriones ob liberalitatem cum esset annorum sexs ordini suo gratis adlegerunt.
"Numerius Popidius Celsinus, son of Numerius, at his own expense rebuilt from its foundations the Temple of Isis, which had been totally destroyed by earthquake. In recognition of his generosity the city council elected him to their

number without any further fee, although he was only six years old."

The ostensible donor was the son of a wealthy freedman of the Popidius family, Numerius Popidius Ampliatus, who was himself debarred from election to the council of decurions because he had been born a slave. There was normally a lower age limit for the decurionate (often twenty-five years), but exceptions could be made, and in this instance the usual admission fee was also waived. Within the sanctuary the father, Ampliatus, was able to dedicate in his own name a statue of Dionysus (here, as often, identified with Osiris); and Celsinus, together with his mother, Corelia Celsa, and a brother, is named as donor of the pavement in the larger of the two rooms beyond the temple.
CIL x. 846; *ILS* 6367.

11,12

11, 12
Plaster casts of two marble reliefs showing scenes of the earthquake of A.D. 62
Lengths 86 cm, heights 13 cm and 17 cm
Lent by Imperial Tobacco Limited
Originals from the House of L. Caecilius Jucundus (V, 1, 26)

The reliefs formed part of the household shrine (*lararium*). Though carved in a strikingly "popular" style, they afford valuable evidence for the appearance of buildings that were still in ruins at the time of the eruption seventeen years later.

The first relief shows the collapse of the Capitolium at the northern end of the Forum (see plan, page 49), its steps flanked by a pair of equestrian statues. On the left is the monumental arch, of which the core still stands, and on the right an altar to Tellus (Earth), which was demolished when the Forum paving was repaired, leaving only traces of its foundations. Around the altar are shown vessels and instruments for the sacrifice of a bull.

The scene on the second relief would have been visible from Caecilius' house. It shows the Vesuvius Gate collapsing, and beside it the main distribution tower for the city's water supply (*castellum aquae*). Although the structure of the latter withstood the tremors, it was still out of action in A.D. 79. Two mules pulling a cart narrowly escape the falling gate, and on the far right, apparently just outside the walls, is a rustic altar beside a tree, presumably a familiar landmark.
Maiuri, *L'ultima fase* 10ff.

13 (not illus.)
Model of the site of Pompeii
Scale 1:250
Lent by Soprintendenza Archeologica delle Province di Napoli e Caserta

The model shows the present state of the excavations of the town, where about two-fifths remains to be uncovered. Little excavation has taken place outside the walls, and any attempts to investigate the immediate surroundings are greatly hampered by the huge mounds of debris from earlier excavations. A great deal more detailed survey work is needed before it will be possible to establish exactly where the ancient coastline and the port of Pompeii lay in relation to the town itself (see map, page 13).

14
Section through the volcanic and later debris covering the site at Pompeii

The successive layers of lava pebbles, pumice stones, ash, and dust that fell on Pompeii vary considerably in depth from point to point within the town, but the general sequence bears out the evidence of Pliny's account of the eruption (see page 37). One of the clearest, least complicated sections through the deposit was recorded on the level, open ground of the Grand Palaestra beside the Amphitheater, excavated in 1938-1939. The deposits associated with the eruption of A.D. 79 were here, on average, just under twelve feet (3.50 m) deep.

Ashy top soil

Lapilli
Ash
Lapilli
Ash

Sandy ash with pieces of carbonized wood
Lapilli
Hardened volcanic sand

Greenish gray pumice

Heavier gray pumice

Light white pumice

Lava pebbles from the plug of the cone, ejected at the beginning of the eruption

14

15

15
Plaster cast of a watchdog
Height 50 cm
Lent by Imperial Tobacco Limited
Original in Pompeii, Antiquarium
From the House of Vesonius Primus (VI, 14, 20)

The unfortunate dog, wearing his bronze-studded collar, was left chained up, and he suffocated beneath the ash and cinders. These then hardened round the corpse, forming an impression that, with the disintegration of the organic remains, became a perfect hollow mold. It was the archaeologist Fiorelli who first realized that by filling such hollow molds with plaster one could obtain faithful replicas of objects such as bodies, wooden doors, furniture, and foodstuffs.

16
Plaster cast of the body of a young woman
Length 1.50 m
Lent by Imperial Tobacco Limited
Original in Pompeii, Antiquarium

Like almost all the other human victims of the eruption, this young woman died of suffocation from the fumes of the falling ash and cinders, which she had vainly tried to keep from her nose and mouth by pulling her tunic up over her face.

16

II The People

17 (color plate, vol. i, p. 18)
Painted portrait of a man and his wife
Height 65 cm, width 58 cm
Naples Museum, inv. 9058
From House VII, 2, 6, on the back wall of
a small *exedra* opening off the atrium

The man, with a short curly beard and
mustache, wears a toga and carries a
papyrus scroll with a red seal. His wife
wears a red tunic and mantle, and her hair
is dressed in a fashion popular about the
middle of the first century A.D. In her right
hand she holds to her lips a *stylus* (see
No. 274) for writing on the two-leaved
wooden tablet spread with wax (*diptych,*
see also No. 243) which she holds in her
left. Although this pose might be thought
to indicate that the subject had literary
tastes, it is found in other contemporary
portraits of young women and is probably
no more than a fashionable painter's con-
vention. Both in style and in treatment
there is a striking resemblance to the
Egyptian mummy portraits of the Roman
period (as, for example, in the National
Gallery, London, no. 2914).

The painting belongs to the last years
of the town, when the house and the adjoining workshop area at the corner of the
insula may have belonged to a person who
was involved in baking or patisserie. The
name long but erroneously associated
with this family portrait is that of Paquius
Proculus, whose name appeared on an
election poster painted on the front of the
house. Subsequent attempts to identify
the owner of the house have been ingeni-
ous rather than convincing.

M. della Corte, *JRS* XVI (1926) 146-154;
E. Drerup, *Die Datierung der Mumienporträts*
(Paderborn 1933) pl. 4.

17

19

18 (color plate, vol. I, p. 20)
Wall painting: portrait of a woman in profile
Height 52 cm, width 39 cm
Naples Museum, inv. 9077
From Herculaneum or Stabiae

Framed portrait from the center of the left-hand lateral panel of a Third Style wall. Old drawings of it show bands of ribbons hanging loosely down from the hair over the shoulders, and the loss of this overpainting accounts for the seeming disproportion of the neck. The same drawings indicate that the hair-band was shown as being made of some precious metal, and that from it sprang delicate sprays of flowers probably executed in pearls and emeralds on gold wire stems. The portrait itself is obviously imitating a cameo, and it has been suggested that it represents Cleopatra.
Pitture di Ercolano IV (1765) 109f., fig. 113; R. Herbig, *Nugae Pompeianorum (Bilderhefte des D.A.I. Rom*, I, 1962) 19f.

19 (color plate, vol. I, p. 19)
Wall painting: figure of a girl
Height 56 cm, width 38.5 cm
Naples Museum, inv. 8946
From Pompeii

The girl sits beside or leans against a column, gazing down at something held in her hands, of which only part is preserved. In her hair she wears an ivy wreath. Although she is probably intended to represent a figure sacrificing or in attendance upon some religious occasion, the head has all the appearance of having been drawn from life.

The fragment comes probably from a Fourth Style architectural composition similar to those in the *cubiculum* of the House of Pinarius Cerealis or in the House of Apollo (see page 100).
Elia 215, fig. 30.

20
Bronze portrait bust of a woman
Height 37 cm
Naples Museum, inv. 4990
From the House of the Citharist (I, 4, 5)

Found in the *ala* of the atrium, together with a similar bronze bust of a man (Naples Museum, inv. 4992; see page 106, left). There is some evidence to suggest that this house, once one of the finest in Pompeii, belonged to the influential local family of the Popidii, and this pair of busts, probably of a man and wife, may well in that case represent members of that family. The analogies for both portraits, including the hairstyles, indicate a date in the early first century A.D. There is another portrait head from Pompeii representing almost certainly the same woman, in marble, slightly over life-size (Naples Museum, inv. 120424, see p. 107). The findspot of this is not recorded, but it

20

clearly comes from a public statue, confirming the suggestion that she belonged to one of the ruling families of the city.

The head was cast in two parts; the looped braid at the nape of the neck was cast separately, and all the finer detail of the hair and eyebrows was worked in with a chisel after casting. A striking and rare feature is the preservation of the original right eye (the left eye is partly restored). The eye sockets were left open in casting and were afterward filled with a very fine white cement, into which were set the lens-shaped pupils, made of a brown, semi-precious stone. The bulging of the eyes is due to the swelling of the cement under the damp conditions of burial.
Kluge-Hartleben II, 22f.; De Franciscis 49f.

18

21

21

Bust of a middle-aged man, perhaps a member of the Popidius family
Rather large-grained, translucent white marble, perhaps from Paros
Height 39 cm
Naples Museum, inv. 6028
Found together with No. 23 in the House of the Citharist (1, 4, 5)

The break across the left shoulder is ancient and was repaired in antiquity with a bronze dowel. The surface of the marble is weathered, suggesting that the bust may have stood originally in a tomb and have been brought to the house for safety after the earthquake of A.D. 62. There are traces of red paint on the hair at the back of the head.

As in the case of No. 23 there have been numerous attempts to identify this as the portrait of some Roman public figure (Pompey, Crassus, Horace, Agrippa, Sejanus, and others), but on balance it is far more likely to be a family portrait connected with the house in which it was found. The form of the bust and the treatment of the hair and facial details indicate a date about the middle of the first century A.D. The workmanship suggests a sculptor from the eastern Mediterranean, based presumably at Puteoli and working for local Campanian patrons.
Fiorelli, *Scavi* 164, no. 147; F. Poulsen, *RM* 29 (1914) 59; De Franciscis 49.

22

Bronze portrait of a young man on a herm shaft
Height overall 1.73 m, height of bust 37.5 cm
Naples Museum, inv. 5584
Probably one of the two bronze busts found in the Basilica at Pompeii in 1813

The surface of the bronze is heavily corroded, and a large fragment is missing from the chest. The pupils of the inlaid eyes have been lost, but the white cement of the right eyeball survives complete, while that on the left is preserved only on the inner corner. Because of the damaged surface it is difficult to assess the original qualities of the workmanship, but it appears that the modeling was rather hard and lifeless by comparison with No. 20 and that less care was taken in engraving the short strands of hair after casting. The herm shaft, which is ancient, may not belong; it is made in lava and stands on a base of tufa.

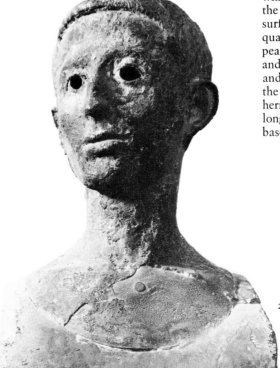

22

The head bears a marked resemblance to the other bronze bust (Naples Museum, inv. "19") considered to have been found with it and also, at least in the unusual quoif of hair over the brow, to the marble portrait of a young man (No. 23) that was found in the House of the Citharist and perhaps represents a member of the Popidius family. The special connection that the Popidii had with the Basilica (see No. 9) may be seen as further evidence to support such an identification.

Fiorelli, *PAH* 1, part 3, 225; De Franciscis 43f.

23 (color plate, vol. 1, p. 17)
Head of a young man, perhaps a member of the Popidius family
Fine-grained white marble, probably from Phrygia in Asia Minor
Height 36.5 cm
Naples Museum, inv. 6025
From the House of the Citharist (1, 4, 5), found together with No. 21 on 19 October 1868 in the stable block, having perhaps fallen from an upper room.

Rough surfaces on the shoulders mark the lines of drapery folds that have been dressed off, indicating that this was probably retrieved from a statue and adapted to a bust after the earthquake of A.D. 62. When found, the nose and ears were damaged and have been restored in plaster, but the repair to the lower lip was made in antiquity, in Italian marble. The hair was probably painted a reddish brown, and the slightly roughened surfaces of the eyeballs may have had the iris and pupil rendered in red and black in the manner usual at this period. The unusually smooth, transparent quality of the flesh surfaces is due to the fine marble, which also permitted the sculptor a greater subtlety and sensitivity of modeling than usual.

The portrait is that of a young man born about the end of the first century B.C., with a quoif of hair over his brow closely resembling that found on No. 22 and in Naples Museum, inv. "19" (see p. 106, right). Scholars have variously identified him with a number of Roman worthies, including the young Marcus Brutus, Agrippa Postumus, or other descendants of Agrippa, Domitius Ahenobarbus, Drusus, son of Germanicus, and there is indeed a close resemblance to a head of unknown provenance in the Capitoline Museum in Rome (Stuart Jones, *Catalogue* pl. 88). But there is also a marked family resemblance to the male bronze from the atrium of the same house (inv. 4992; see page 106, left) and to the bronze head from the Basilica, and it seems far more likely that this is a member of the local family to whom this house belonged, usually identified as the Popidii.

Fiorelli, *Scavi* 164, no. 148; F. Poulsen, *Ikonografische Miscellen* (Copenhagen 1921) 57ff.; L. Curtius, *RM* 47 (1932) 228f.; De Franciscis 47.

23

24

24

Epitaph of Titus Terentius Felix, a city magistrate
Marble
Width 53 cm, height 38.5 cm
Naples Museum, inv. 3879
Found in 1763 just outside the Herculaneum Gate, where there is now a reproduction.

T[ito] Terentio T[iti] f[ilio] Men[enia tribu] Felici maiori aedil[i]. Huic publice locus datus et HS ∞ ∞. Fabia Probi f[ilia] Sabina uxor.
"To Titus Terentius Felix senior, son of Titus, of the tribe Menenia, aedile. The site [of this monument] was presented to him by the city together with the sum of 2000 sesterces. It was erected by his wife, Fabia Sabina, daughter of Probus."

Terentius Felix may have died as a relatively young man, possibly while holding the junior magistracy of the aedileship, which would account for the contribution from public funds toward the cost of his monument. He appears as first witness to one of the documents of Lucius Caecilius Jucundus in the period preceding the earthquake of A.D. 62. The Terentii were an old Italic family long established in Campania. His wife too came from an old family, the Fabii, most of the known Pompeian representatives of which were freedmen engaged in the wine trade. Another Titus Terentius (Felix junior?), who may well have been his son, was a candidate for the aedileship in the last period of the city.

CIL X. 1019; Castrén, no. 402,9; Andreau 209, 321.

25

Bronze portrait bust of a young man
Height 42.5 cm
Naples Museum, inv. 5617
From Pompeii

The surface of the bronze appears severely cleaned, and the eyes have been given a modern inlay of silver and copper to replace the ancient cement and glass. Although the work is technically competent, and great care went into the secondary working of detail in the hair and eyebrows after casting, the portrait lacks the character and individuality of most of the other Pompeian bronzes, having more in common with the rather cold academicism of many of the Herculaneum portrait busts (e.g., Naples Museum, inv. 5632). It has often been identified as a youthful portrait of the emperor Tiberius (born 42 B.C., died A.D. 37), but there is little to support this identification beyond the arrangement of the locks of hair over his brow. The form of the bust indicates, rather, a somewhat later date, about the middle of the first century A.D.

De Franciscis 42f., fig. 34; L. Polacco, *Il Volto di Tiberio* (Rome 1955) 184, no. 6.

25

26
Portrait bust of an old man
Pentelic marble
Height 37.8 cm
Naples Museum, inv. 6169
From Pompeii

The gaunt face, with its hooked nose and projecting ears, a type one can still see among Neapolitans today, is uncompromisingly realistic. It is a good example of a long-lived and popular style of Roman portrait sculpture whose origins can be sought in the various trends current in the late Republic, but which prevailed far into the first century A.D. The carving of the eyes and hair and the treatment of the flesh surfaces show that it was probably made in the first quarter of the first century A.D.

Although its original location is not recorded, the cutting of the bust shows that it was mounted on a herm shaft, perhaps to stand beside the entrance to the *tablinum* in a Pompeian house.
B. Schweitzer, *Die Bildniskunst der römischen Republik* (Leipzig 1948) 115, 119;
A. N. Zadoks-Josephus Jitta, *Ancestral Portraiture in Rome* (Amsterdam 1932) 54, 67; De Franciscis 40f.

27

27
Male portrait head
Gray coarse-grained limestone
Height 24 cm
Pompeii, Antiquarium, inv. P. 76/147

The head is broken off from a life-sized statue, which has apparently not been found, but which probably stood in a tomb outside the walls of Pompeii. It is worked in a hard, linear style characteristic of the local central Italian tradition and in marked contrast to the contemporary "Roman" portraiture represented by Nos. 20, 25. The hair is treated as a formal pattern and the ears almost as abstract designs; facial details like the wrinkles on the brow and the lines in the jowls are equally reduced to a severe symmetry. The faint half-smile of the lips appears all the more expressive as a result.

28
Terracotta statuette of a tipsy old woman
Height 39.5 cm
Naples Museum, inv. 124844
From House VI, 15, 5

The subject, well known in later Hellenistic sculpture, pottery, and terracotta, may be derived from a statue by Myron that was set up at Smyrna (Izmir) in Asia Minor. The almost toothless old woman is shown seated, with hair and clothing disheveled, grumbling to herself and clutching the bottom half of a wine amphora, of which the top half lies beside her foot. The figure is hollow and is adapted to serve as a jug. On the back is a filling hole at the nape of the neck and the remains of a handle. Her mouth was the spout. Mid-first century A.D.

This piece was found in the fountain niche at the far side of the garden peristyle, together with two glazed terracotta statuettes, a marble statuette of a nymph, and another terracotta figurine of similar size representing an elephant carrying a tower (Naples Museum, inv. 124845).
NSc 1897, 23f.; Levi 197, no. 849.

29
Terracotta doll
Height 17.5 cm
Naples Museum, inv. 123971
From Pompeii

Schematic female figure, with tall conical body and a tiny knob-like head, perhaps a simple child's toy. The details of her dress are added in red paint.
Levi no. 870.

29

26

28

37
Small bronze bust of the emperor Augustus

Height (excluding the modern base)
13.4 cm
Naples Museum, inv. 5473
From Herculaneum, 26 October 1752

The first Roman emperor is portrayed in a variant of his most popular official portrait type, best known from the statue found in the Villa of Livia at Prima Porta (Vatican, Braccio Nuovo 14). The little bust, which is hollow cast, was made after his death, probably in the reign of Tiberius or Claudius, and was possibly dedicated in a shrine of the Imperial cult somewhere near the Theater.

P. Zanker, *Studien zu den Augustus-Porträts. I. Der Actium-Typus* (Göttingen 1973) 32, no. 20.

39

37

38
Bronze statue of Lucius Mammius Maximus

Height 2.12 m
Naples Museum, inv. 5591
From Herculaneum, found in the Theater on 24 December 1743.

The statue, which honors a wealthy benefactor of Herculaneum (see No. 39) was found, together with its marble pedestal and bronze dedicatory inscription, on the highest level of the auditorium of the Theater. It is hollow cast in a rich copper bronze. The head and neck, the left hand, the right forearm, part of the drapery, and the two feet were cast separately. The casting is technically accomplished, and the surfaces have been very carefully worked over to remove traces of the processes of casting and assembly and to correct minor blemishes. The head is a portrait and was certainly modeled by a different sculptor, probably from a different workshop and working to order.

Bronze public statuary was common in antiquity, but the vast majority has since disappeared into the melting pot. Large bronze statues such as this are very rare survivals, and it is in marble sculpture that one has to look for parallels. Stylistically the head of Mammius closely resembles the portrait statue of Fundilius, an actor, found at Nemi and now in Copenhagen. The arrangement of the toga, too, closely resembles that on the Fundilius statue and on another piece found in the theater at Caere (Cerveteri), a mode that appears to date from the years immediately following the middle of the first century. This fits well with the likely date of Mammius himself.

Venuti, *Heraclea* 75; Kluge-Hartleben II 65ff.; Goethert, *RM* 54 (1939) 240f.

39
Bronze dedicatory inscription
Height 70 cm, width 45 cm
Naples Museum, inv. 3748
Found at Herculaneum, attached to the marble base of No. 38.

L. Mammio Maximo Augustali municipes et incolae aere conlato.

"To Lucius Mammius Maximus, Augustalis, [this statue is erected] by the citizens and other residents, by public subscription."

The name of L. Mammius Maximus figures on a number of other inscriptions at Herculaneum, three of which (*CIL* x. 1, 1413, 1417, 1418) record dedications to Livia, who was deified by the emperor Claudius, to Antonia, his mother, and to Agrippina, his niece and the mother of Nero; a fourth (*CIL* x. 1. 1451), recording an unspecified donation to the city, and a fifth (*CIL* x. 1, 1450), his construction or restoration of a market building *(macellum)* and his giving of a public banquet on the occasion of its dedication. The Mammii (sometimes spelled Mamii) were an old Samnite family, represented also at Pompeii, where they were one of the first non-colonist families to achieve public office after 80 B.C., at Capua, at Aquinum, and in the mountains of Samnium. It was a relative or connection of this family, L. Annius Mammianus Rufus, who built the Theater at Herculaneum, probably under Augustus (*CIL* x. 1, 1443-1445). As an Augustalis, Mammius Maximus was almost certainly a freedman, which would accord with his failure to mention his father's name. Born the slave of a powerful, land-owning family, it was doubtless with the family's support that as a freedman, like Petronius' Trimalchio, he achieved great wealth and, by his lavish use of it, achieved high civic honor.

CIL x. 1, 1452; *ILS* 6352. For the Mammii, see Castrén 188, no. 237.

38

40 (color plate, vol. I, p. 31)
Gold bulla
Length 6.5 cm, weight 14.08 grams
Naples Museum, inv. 145490
From the House of the Menander (I, 10, 4)

The *bulla,* a small bag-shaped amulet, was
worn around the neck, a practice the
Romans derived from the Etruscans,
among whom it seems to have been worn
as an ornament by both sexes. Among the
Romans the gold *bulla* (sometimes known
as *Etruscum aureum*) took on a more re-
stricted significance, being worn from in-
fancy by the sons of citizens as a visible
token of free birth. On coming of age and
formally assuming the dress of manhood
(the *toga virilis*), it was customary to lay
the *bulla* ceremoniously aside in the
household *lararium* (see No. 210). At a
later date its use was permitted also to
the sons of freedmen.

This example is shaped in the form of a
miniature pouch, with a lens-shaped body
made of two plain convex discs, riveted to
an elaborately ornamented flap, through
which passed the small suspension ring of
beaded gold wire. The decoration of the
flap is symmetrical about a central braid
made up of two ribbons, each of three
strands of gold wire plaited and framed
between two pairs of counter-twisted
wire, which are arranged so as to convey
the impression of a minute chain of heart-
shaped links. This frame is continued
round the plain fields to right and left of
the central braid. Along the junction of
the flap and the body are pendant triangles of gold beading.

This handsome piece was found in the
House of the Menander, together with
several other pieces of fine jewelry, in the
same wooden chest as the famous set of
silver plate (see page 109).

Maiuri, *Menandro* 381, no. 127; Breglia
no. 918; Siviero no. 340.

41 (withdrawn from exhibition)
Gold finger ring with sardonyx cameo
Naples Museum, inv. 25181

42
Gold ring with sardonyx intaglio
Diameter 1.8 cm
Naples Museum, inv. 111775
From Pompeii

The heavy gold ring with an inset stone
is of a very common Roman form. The
finely cut intaglio shows the profile of a
curly-haired, Hermes-like youth in a
courtly classicistic style. The head is cut
through from a light into a dark-colored
layer of the stone, with strikingly decorative effect.

Breglia no. 532, pl. XXIX, 7; Siviero no. 410,
pl. 228 a.

40

42

43

44

43
Gold serpent ring
Diameter 2.1 cm
Naples Museum, inv. 25041
From Herculaneum

This ring, in the form of a serpent wound
around the finger, is a reduced version of
armbands like No. 48, where a simple spi-
raling body with incised scales terminates
in a powerfully modeled head.

Breglia no. 678; Siviero no. 220, pl. 169 e.

44
Pair of cluster earrings
Gold, pearls, and green plasma
Length 2.8 cm and 3.0 cm
Naples Museum, inv. 25266 and 25267
From one of the sites in the Vesuvius area

The center of each flower-like cluster consists of an oval cabouchon of green plasma
set in a gold frame edged with gold beads.
Radiating from it are sixteen petals, consisting alternately of shaped gold sheet
and of irregularly shaped pearls set on
pegs of gold wire. A globule of mother-of-
pearl hangs from the bottom-most gold
petal. A large gold hook is soldered to the
back. First century B.C. to first century A.D.

Breglia nos. 226, 227; Siviero no. 307.

45
Gold and pearl earrings
Length 3.3 cm
Naples Museum, inv. 145482
From the House of the Menander

The pearls are threaded onto a gold wire armature; six rows, with a transverse reinforcement, form a dome-like cluster. This type of earring, sometimes made with stones or glass paste beads, is common at Pompeii and Herculaneum. Its shape varies from the rigidly geometrical to more irregular forms suggesting bunches of grapes.

Maiuri, *Menandro* 380, no. 119, pl. LXV; A. Morassi, *Antica oreficeria italiana* (1936) 22, nos. 32, 33; Breglia 59, nos. 236, 237, pl. XXXIII, 7, 8; Siviero no. 283, pl. 190, color pl. 189.

46
Gold earrings
Length 2.7 cm and 2.5 cm
Naples Museum, inv. 116077
From Pompeii or Herculaneum

Numerous variants of this neat, elegant form of earring come from the cities destroyed by Vesuvius. The fashion apparently ran from the first century B.C. through the first century A.D. The simple dome shape with a much smaller disc (or in other versions, a bead) attached to its edge is here enhanced by granulated decoration.

Breglia 59-60, no. 278, pl. XXX; Siviero no. 278, pl. 186 a.

47

48

45

46

47 (color plate, vol. I, p. 32)
Gold armband in the form of a snake
Diameter 8 cm, length 11 cm
Naples Museum, inv. 24824
Probably found at Pompeii

One of a pair of armbands, each shaped from a flat ribbon of gold on which the scales were indicated with a V-shaped punch. The head was cast separately, and the eyes were originally set with green vitreous paste. First century B.C. to first century A.D.

MB 7 (Rome 1831) pl. XLVI; Breglia no. 827; Siviero no. 202.

48
Gold snake armband
Diameter 8.1 cm
Naples Museum, inv. 24772
From Pompeii

This snake armband is one of a pair, as such pieces usually were. The body has been schematized into a simple, regular spiral with a circular cross-section. The incised scales have been omitted in the central part of the two turns. The powerfully modeled and incised head with its gaping jaws has, however, a striking reptilian vitality. The eyes were originally filled with green glass paste.

Breglia no. 831; Siviero no. 203, pl. 160.

49
Gold pin with head in the form of a cantharus
Length 13 cm
Naples Museum, inv. 145488
From the House of the Menander

This hair ornament is a pin topped with a miniature cantharus (drinking cup) of Hellenistic form. It is enriched with beaded decoration and topped by a light-colored glass paste "jewel."

Maiuri, *Menandro* 381, no. 126, pl. LXV; Breglia no. 924, pl. XXXIII, 21; Siviero no. 135, pl. 126.

50 (color plate, vol. I, p. 32)
Gold bracelet
Diameter 8.3 cm
Naples Museum, inv. 109587
From House I, 2, 3

Two lengths of thick gold wire loosely intertwined to form eight large loops, soldered together at the crossings; over one of these is an applied gold ornament. First century B.C. to first century A.D.

Breglia no. 868; Siviero no. 238.

49

50

51

52

51
Gold bracelet
Length 25.2 cm
Naples Museum, inv. 136792
From Pompeii

The bracelet was found with the skeleton of a person who was attempting to flee, carrying a casket of jewelry. Looter or owner, he or she had waited too long, until the ash had accumulated some ten feet deep, then climbed out of the building from an upper-story window and after a few steps dropped dead, scattering the precious objects. The bracelet is made up of links, each consisting of two gold domes joined by a double row of beaded ornament and connected with the next link by two loops. A leaf-shaped clasp fastens the bracelet, which was one of a pair and belongs to a type often found at Pompeii.

V. Spinazzola, "Rinvenimenti di due scheletri e di oggetti preziosi," in *NSc* 1914, 207, fig. 2; Breglia no. 860; Siviero no. 250, pl. 179 b.

52 (color plate, vol. 1, p. 32)
Part of a necklace of gold ivy leaves
Length 53 cm
Naples Museum, inv. 111114
From Pompeii, 9 June 1877

The necklace consisted originally of two concentric bands of ivy leaves stamped out of sheet gold and linked to each other by tiny loops of gold wire; the loops are masked by small gold bosses. The 48 leaves of this piece converge symmetrically upon a large convex gold disc. Its companion piece (Naples, inv. 111113) contained 46 leaves but was otherwise identical. The clasp that joined the two bands behind the neck is missing. The form, rare in Roman jewelry, probably derives from the Hellenistic world. First century B.C. to first century A.D.

Breglia no. 478; Siviero no. 166.

53
Gold necklace
Length 2.52 m
Naples Museum, inv. 25260
Probably from Pompeii

The long chain of delicately interwoven links is interrupted only by two wheel-like ornaments, one of which functions as a clasp. From the chain hangs a small crescent-shaped pendant. Both the wheel and the lunar crescent, though primarily decorative here, can have implications of love-magic and so are especially suited to feminine adornment.

Spinazzola 226; Breglia no. 483; Siviero no. 168, pls. 138, 139.

54

Gold pendant

Height of figure 2 cm, length with chain
5.5 cm
Naples Museum, inv. 24673
From Herculaneum

The nude baby pours from a vessel in his
raised left hand to the bowl in his right.
This is the gesture of the little household
god, the Lar, but also of a festive cup
bearer. His hair is dressed in bunches of
ringlets over his ears.

Spinazzola 226; Breglia no. 183, pl. XXII, 1;
Siviero no. 142, pl. 129 b.

55

**Gold mesh necklace set with emeralds
and pearls**

Length 34.5 cm
Naples Museum, inv. 113576
From the seaside suburb of Pompeii
(contrada Bottaro)

Large, irregular stones, alternately emeralds and baroque pearls, are superimposed
on an exquisitely made gold mesh, rein-
forced with larger dots of gold where the
links cross. This taste for openwork and
for light, abstract, bubbly forms character-
izes much jewelry found at Pompeii and
amounts to a fashion trend of Imperial
times, away from the modeled, often representational elements of Greek jewelry.
Since the mesh and the clasp are obviously
the work of a superb craftsman, the use of
the stones with large simple shapes must
have been deliberate and carefully
thought out.

NSc 1881, 27; Spinazzola 226; Breglia 62,
no. 473, pl. 31, 2; Siviero no. 164, pl. 133.

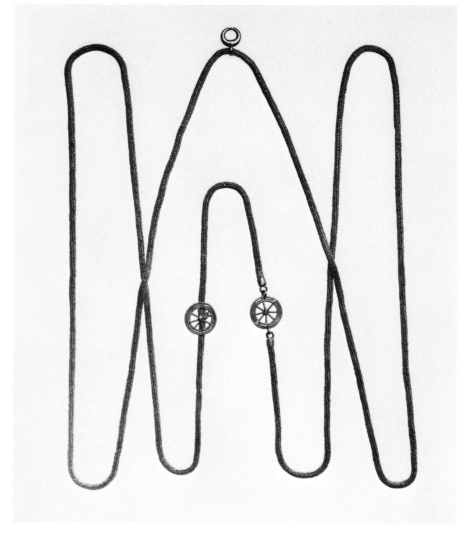

53

54

55

56

57

56
Silver hand mirror
Diameter 10.5 cm, length of handle 11 cm
Naples Museum, inv. 76/243
From one of the sites in the Vesuvius area

The reflecting disc of the mirror has a
cusped border. The back bears a simple
decoration of engraved concentric circles.
The looped form of the handle is unusual.

For similar forms, see Mau-Kelsey 372-373,
fig. 205; Strong 157.

57
Silver hand mirror
Diameter 11 cm, length of handle 9.3 cm
Naples Museum, inv. 25716
From Pompeii

A very common form of hand mirror. The
back is decorated with concentric circles
and a border of palmettes edged with two
rows of beaded dots. The baluster handle
is one of the two most usual types, the
other being in the shape of a club of
Hercules.

Strong 157.

58
Silver hand mirror
Height 34 cm
Naples Museum, inv. 145524
From the House of the Menander

This silver hand mirror is decorated on
the back with a separately made *emblema*
of a profile female head in repoussé. The
idea of the profile head goes back to those
in high relief on the outside of Greek
mirror covers. The head shown here, however, with its delicate technique, its ex-
tremely refined and precise beauty, seems
more influenced by Greek coins or, as has
been suggested, by the gem cutter's work,
which reached such perfection in late
Republican and early Imperial times. Like
many *emblemata*, it was probably copied
by the silversmith from a plaster cast of a
famous model; a number of these casts
have come down to us. The form and
ornament of the mirror are completely
Roman, with bold and, in its way, very
pure use of flat, cutout shapes, piercing,
and turned elements.

Maiuri, *Menandro* 350ff., no. 15, pls. XLVII,
XLVIII.

59
Fragment of a bone hair comb
Width 6.1 cm, surviving length 8 cm
Naples Museum, inv. 119990
From a *cubiculum* off the atrium in House
IX, 6, 5

Combs in antiquity, made of ivory or
bone, were normally of this shape, with
teeth down both long sides. As in many
modern combs, the teeth are spaced dif-
ferently, about seven to the centimeter on
one side and about fourteen on the other.
Similar combs have been found in some
numbers at Pompeii, among them one that
is painted with a design of two ducks in
red, black, and white.

Mau-Kelsey 371.

59

58

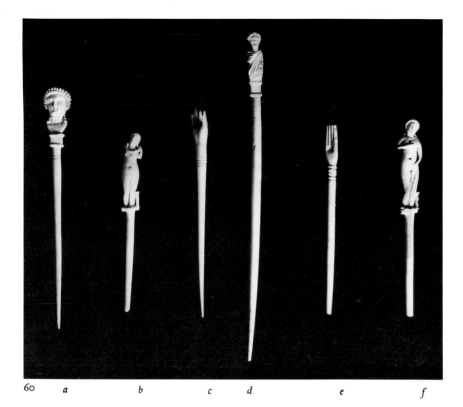

60   *a*   *b*   *c*   *d*   *e*   *f*

61

60
Six hairpins with variously decorated finials

a. Bust of a female divinity. Ivory
Length 13.2 cm
Naples Museum, inv. 77441
From Pompeii
b. Aphrodite (Venus) tying her hair. Ivory
Length 9.8 cm
Naples Museum, inv. 121730
From the corridor beside the *tablinum* in the House of the Cenaculum (v, 2, Mau D).
c. Hand with fingers spread. Ivory
Length 11.6 cm
Naples Museum, old inv. 9326
From Pompeii
d. Male herm wearing a mantle (*himation*)
Bone
Length 18.2 cm
Naples Museum, old inv. 9272
From Pompeii
e. Hand with fingers together. Ivory
Length 10.3 cm
Naples Museum, old inv. 9327
From Pompeii
f. Pudicitia, personification of modesty and chastity. Bone
Length 10.8 cm
Naples Museum, old inv. 9270
From Pompeii

Many Roman hairstyles involved the use of tight curls made with hot tongs, and some of these pins would have been toilet instruments, used for arranging the hair rather than as ornaments or for fastening the hair in place.
Mau-Kelsey 372, fig. 203.

61 (cover illus.)
Mosaic portrait of a woman

Height 25.5 cm, width 20.5 cm
Naples Museum, inv. 124666
From a small *cubiculum* in House VI, 15, 14

Portrait, probably from life, of a young woman. Her hair is parted centrally and tied behind with a ribbon. She wears earrings of pearls set in gold, a pearl necklace with a gold clasp set with precious stones, and a dark, low-necked dress, which shows through a gold-embroidered transparent veil. Dress and jewelry suggest a woman of rank.

This is a studio piece (*emblema*) made with very small tesserae, shaped and toned, set within a shallow, tray-like limestone frame. It was found in the center of an *opus sectile* pavement made up of hexagons, lozenges, and triangles of blue-gray, white, and red marble, dating from the last period before A.D. 79. In this context it was almost certainly reused. The mosaic itself can hardly be later than the end of the first century B.C.
A. Sogliano, *NSc* 1898, 171ff.; A. Mau, *RM* 16 (1901) 283f.; Pernice VI, 88 and 178-179.

III The Garden

62

62

Large Neo-Attic vase (crater)
Pentelic marble
Height 82 cm, diameter at the rim 65 cm
Naples Museum, inv. 6778
From Stabiae

Both the form and much of the decoration
of this vase derive closely from metalwork
prototypes, commonly reproduced also in
South Italian bronzeware and in the fine
South Italian pottery. The figured decoration is Dionysiac in inspiration. On one
side is Dionysus himself, portrayed in the
Archaic manner, holding a jug and a
thyrsus and leading personifications of
Summer and Autumn; on the other side
are Spring and Winter with a satyr. At the
junctions of the tall volute handles with
the body are Silenus heads.

Some of the best Athenian craftsmen of
the later first century B.C. were engaged in
producing large marble vases of this sort.
They were normally used as garden
ornaments.

63

Dionysiac herm in colored marbles
Height 87 cm
Naples Museum, inv. 126252
From Pompeii

The head is that of an elderly Silenus, one
of the drinking companions of Dionysus,
shown wreathed with ivy berries. The
slightly tapering shaft stands on two bare
human feet, carved out of the same block
of white Italian marble as the base, which
in its turn is veneered with profiled moldings and a deeply cusped facing slab. A
narrow rectangular pillar runs up the back
of the herm. The head, shaft, and pillar
are of colored marbles imported from
Imperial quarries overseas: the head, of
yellow Numidian marble, *giallo antico,*
from Simitthu (the modern Chemtou) in
northwestern Tunisia; the shaft and base
moldings, of purple and cream variegated
marble from Skyros, an island in the north
Aegean; the pillar, of green and white
marble, *cipollino,* from Euboea off the
eastern coast of Greece.

A herm of this sort was probably used
as a table support (cf. No. 113) in a peristyle or garden.

63

64

65

64
Oscillum in the form of a theater mask
Italian marble
Height 36 cm
Naples Museum, inv. 6613
From Pompeii

Oscilla hung between the columns of a
peristyle garden; see also Nos. 65, 69, 75,
78. The mask, that of a heroine in Greek
tragedy, is distinguished by sloping
brows, wavy hair, and a low *onkos*. First
century A.D.

MB 7 (Rome 1843) pl. VIII; Bieber, *Theater*,
fig. 567; Webster, *Tragedy and Satyr Play* 85,
NS 5.

65
Theater mask in high relief
Italian marble
Height 31 cm
Naples Museum, inv. 6611
From Pompeii

Though possibly made to be hung as an
oscillum, this mask was probably set in a
wall, as in the garden of the House of
Neptune and Amphitrite at Herculaneum.
With its tall, rounded peak and hair falling in corkscrew curls, this would appear
to be a mask from Tragedy. The fillet
(ribbon) across the brow, with two dangling ends, and the wreath of ivy leaves
and berries suggest specifically Dionysiac
associations.

MB 7 (Rome 1843) pl. VIII.

66

66
**Rectangular panel with theater masks in
relief**
Pentelic marble
Height 25.5 cm, width 33 cm
Naples Museum, inv. 6619
From Pompeii

The panel, which is carved on both faces,
probably stood on a small column in a
Pompeian garden similar to that of the
House of the Gilded Cupids, or Amorini
(see page 55). In high relief on one side are
masks belonging to stock characters in
Greek New Comedy: on the right, the
scheming, impudent, leading slave; and
on the left, the delicately brought-up
youth *(hapalos)*, suitor for the hand of the
daughter of the old man whose mask lies
below. Beyond the youth, in low relief, is
the mask of a satyr, and on the other face
of the panel, again in low relief, those of
an elderly Silenus *(papposilenos)* and of a
young satyr.
Bieber, *Theater* 155; Webster, *New Comedy*
194, NS 17.

67

68

69

67
Rectangular panel with theater masks in relief
Pentelic marble
Height 29.5 cm, width 40 cm
Naples Museum, inv. 6633
From Pompeii

The panel is carved on both sides and, like No. 66, was probably mounted on a low column. In high relief on the front are masks from Greek New Comedy: a delicate youth, a curly-bearded old man (top right), and a leading slave (bottom left). In the background is a temple front in low relief. A large fragment missing from the bottom right-hand corner may have contained a fourth mask, of an angry youth, as on a similar relief from Ostia. On the reverse of the panel, facing one another in low relief, are two masks of Tragedy, laid on rocks, both with high *onkoi*. One is accompanied by a sword and probably represents a hero, the other is a woman with a large kerchief covering her hairpiece and side-locks.

MB 8 (Naples 1844) pl. XLVII; Bieber, *Theater* 155f.; Webster, *New Comedy* 195, NS 22; idem, *Tragedy and Satyr Play* 92, NS 8.

68
Bronze fountain figure of a raven
Height 26 cm, length 58 cm
Naples Museum, inv. 4891
From a villa at Stabiae, not found in position

Hollow cast, the wings cast separately and added. The water pipe led in under the tail and out through the mouth. The raven was one of the attributes of Apollo, many of whose sanctuaries were built around springs.

Kapossy, *Brunnenfiguren* 52; Ruggiero, *Stabia*, p. viii, villa no. 1; *MB* 8 (Rome 1844) pl. LIII.

69
Circular oscillum
Italian marble
Diameter 34 cm
Naples Museum, inv. 6647
From the peristyle garden of the House of the Black Wall (VII, 4, 59)

An *oscillum* was an ornament freely suspended by a chain from the architrave between the columns of a peristyle. On one side of this example is carved in low relief a figure of the youthful Hercules, a lion skin about his shoulders and carrying a club and bow; in front of him runs a boar, the sacrificial animal proper to his cult. On the other side an elderly Pan plays his pipes beside a tree, from which hangs a goatskin bag of fruit.

F. G. Welcker, *Alte Denkmäler* II (Göttingen 1848), 132, no. 40; *MemErc* III (1843) 238.

70

70
Bronze fountain group: two hounds attacking a boar
Height 50 cm, maximum width 1.22 m
Naples Museum, inv. 4899, 4900, 4901
From the House of the Citharist (I, 4, 5)

The group, which derives from Hellenistic
animal sculpture, stood between bronze
figures of a snake, a deer, and a lion on
the semi-circular fountain basin in the
middle peristyle. Water gushed into the
pool from a pipe in the boar's mouth and
also, it seems, from the mouth of the
hound on the right, which is trying to bite
the boar's leg. The front paws of the
hound on the left were fixed to the side of
the boar by rivets. Tails and ears were cast
separately, and great care went into the
working of such secondary details as the
boar's hide. The group is among the liveli-
est pieces of sculpture found at Pompeii.
Kapossy, *Brunnenfiguren* 48.

71
Rectangular panel with theater masks in relief
White Italian marble
Height 29.5 cm, width 39.5 cm
Naples Museum, inv. 6631
From Pompeii

The panel, carved on both sides, was
probably set up in a garden (as No. 65). In
relief on the front, and resting on a rocky
shelf, are masks that derive from those
used in the Greek Satyr Play: on the left
Dionysus and on the right a maenad. Both
are treated in the Archaic style. An unusual feature is that, instead of the large
drill holes normally used for the pupils of
such masks, the eyes are blank and were
presumably painted. On the reverse, in
very low relief, are the masks of a Silenus
and a satyr.
Bieber, *Theater* 158.

72
Fountain figure: boy with dolphin
Italian marble
Height 49 cm
Naples Museum, inv. 6112
From the peristyle of House IX, 2, 27

The boy sits on a small base, his right
hand on the dolphin's head, his left holding the tail, watching the water pouring
from the dolphin's mouth. The hair and
eyebrows were painted red, and red paint
was used also to indicate the eyelashes
and the iris, with the pupil marked by a
black dot. The figure belongs to a large
series of small children and Erotes riding
dolphins or clutching amphorae, shells,
dolphins, frogs, hares, ducks, or doves,
variously adapted as fountain jets. It was
made in Campania, about the middle of
the first century A.D.
Fiorelli, *Scavi* 165, no. 159; Kapossy,
Brunnenfiguren 42.

73
Fountain figure: Cupid on dolphin
Marble
Height 40.5 cm
Pompeii, Antiquarium, inv. 2084/4
From the House of Ceres (I, 9, 13)

An agile, diminutive Cupid perches side-
saddle on a plunging dolphin. The workmanship is dainty, lively, playful, with an
interesting rendering of the waves splash-
ing around the dolphin's head. The group
is one of four such pieces from the House
of Ceres.
Kapossy, *Brunnenfiguren* 39.

71

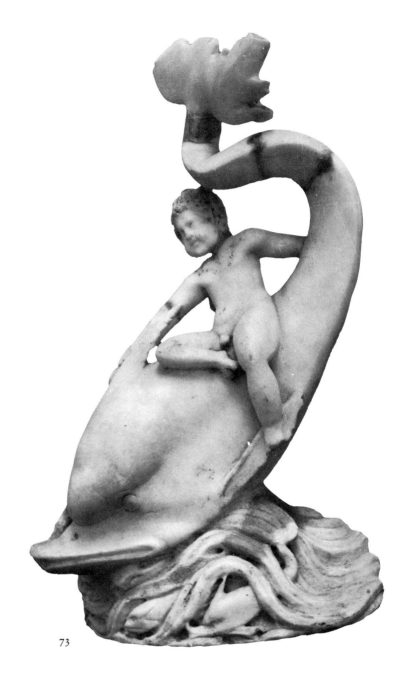

73

72

74
Herm of Hercules
Yellow marble *(giallo antico)*, from
Tunisia
Height 80 cm
Naples Museum, inv. 6383
From Herculaneum

Hercules is portrayed as bearded and
wearing a large lion skin wrapped around
him like a cloak, a type that seems to date
back to Greek sculpture of the fourth century B.C. The head, body, and base are
carved separately in three different qualities of the same stone. Close parallels are
found in other colored stones: one from
Sparta in red Laconian marble *(rosso
antico)* and another, also from Herculaneum but adapted as a table support, in a
black and red marble *(africano)* from
western Turkey.
Cf. Daremberg and Saglio, s. v. *Hercules*
fig. 3802.

75
Pelta-shaped oscillum
Italian marble
Height 22.5 cm, width 37 cm
Naples Museum, inv. 6664
From Pompeii

An angular version of the *pelta,* the traditional shield of the Amazons. The central
projection from which it hung is carved as
a palmette, and the outer ends of the crescent as griffins' heads. Rather simply
carved in low relief within the field are a
bird eating cherries and, on the opposite
face, a basket of fruit.

76
Bronze fountain figure of a bull
Length 51 cm, height 39 cm
Naples Museum, inv. 4890
From the atrium of the House of the
Bull (v, 1, 7)

Hollow cast, with the short horns, ears and
tail added separately, the bull is shown as
a young and powerful animal. Though
perhaps a purely ornamental piece, it
would have had associations with several
well-known divinities, including Zeus (see
No. 129), Poseidon, and Dionysus. The
figure stood on the edge of the *impluvium*
basin in the center of the atrium, water
spouting from the jet in his mouth. Although interior fountains had been a feature of the large Campanian country villas
since the first century B.C. (e.g., the Villa
of the Papyri at Herculaneum), their appearance in the town houses of Pompeii
is a late phenomenon.
Niccolini III, pl. 21; Kapossy, *Brunnenfiguren*
53.

74

75

76

77
Archaising female herm
White Italian marble
Height 96 cm
Naples Museum, inv. 126251
From Pompeii

The figure of a woman, possibly a Muse, in the Archaic Greek manner, has been adapted to the form of a herm. She wears a fillet in her hair, and her long tunic, tied with a knotted girdle below her breasts, is carved in shallow relief on the three flat sides of the herm shaft. The eyes are hollowed out for inlay.

The shaft is socketed into a heavy block of lava, and a pillar of travertine runs up the back of the herm to a point slightly above the head. The herm was probably used as a table support in a garden or in a peristyle corridor.

78

77

79

78
Oscillum in the form of a theater mask
Italian marble
Height 29 cm
Naples Museum, inv. 6618
From Pompeii

The *oscillum,* one of a pair, is in the form of a theatrical mask of a youth from Greek New Comedy, distinguished by a roll of corkscrew curls and hanging corkscrew locks. At the top are the remains of the bronze rod by which it was hung from the architrave of the peristyle. First century A.D.

MB 7 (Rome 1843) pl. VIII; Webster, *New Comedy* (1969) 194, NS 16.

79
Wall painting of a garden
Length 1.25 m, height 35.5 cm
Pompeii, Antiquarium, inv. 1200-4
From the western portico of the Villa Imperiale, near the Porta Marina

Part of the dado of the Third Style decoration of the back wall of the portico. The garden, a rectangular enclosure with low trelliswork walls, is shown as if viewed obliquely from above. The façade is symmetrical around a wide central opening flanked by a pair of tall pillars bearing vases. These frame a square pool with a central fountain figure set on a pedestal. Two identical pillars mark the outer corners of the façade, and midway between the right-hand and left-hand pairs of pillars are two square, openwork pavilions. The side walls of the enclosure are plain. The rear wall echoes the scheme of the façade, with a central *aedicula* flanked by two trellis-vaulted arbors. The vegetation within the garden is indicated schematically by a line of trees immediately behind the front wall.

Cf. P. Grimal, *Les jardins romains* (Paris 1969) 265f.

80

80 (color plate, vol. I, p. 28)
Wall painting of a garden
Length 1.37 m, height 32 cm
Naples Museum, inv. 9964
From Herculaneum

This scene, probably from the dado of a
wall of the late Third or Fourth Style,
shows one side of a garden enclosure, the
trellised fence of which is laid out symmetrically around three semi-circular
exedrae. Midway between the latter are
two passageways arched over with trelliswork, while at the two ends of the composition there are two rectangular openwork arbors planted with vines. Fountain
basins set on pedestals stand at the en-
trances to the passages, and at four points
along the fence taller, trellised posts support large, slender, bronze-colored vases.
Five long-legged, stork-like birds complete the scene.

 Most of the elements of this sort of
fenced garden are already present in the
Garden Room paintings from the Villa of
Livia at Prima Porta (see page 96), and
they recur in varying combinations in
many Pompeian paintings (see No. 79).
The type was evidently firmly established
in painting. This does not, of course, pre-
clude the use of similarly fenced formal
gardens in the *villae marittimae* of Campania. Real gardening and painted representations of gardens are two aspects of a
common tradition.
Pitture di Ercolano I, 239; MB 9 (Rome 1845)
576, pl. LXXXVI; P. Grimal, *Les jardins
romains* (Paris 1969) 267.

81
Wall painting: part of a garden
Height 80 cm, width 80 cm
Naples Museum, inv. 9705
From Pompeii

This painting and its companion pieces
(Naples Museum, inv. 8723, 8762, and
"9710") come probably from the walls of
a small garden enclosure *(viridarium)* or
covered garden room. A large fluted fountain bowl stands in the re-entrant recess
of a wooden fence, on the rail of which a
bird is perched, trying to drink from the
fountain jet. Beyond the fence is dark
foliage of trees or bushes, and in the foreground are the faded traces of low, iris-
like plants.
H. Roux Aîné, *Herculanum et Pompéi* V
(Paris 1870) 98, pl. 52.

81

82
Statue of Artemis in the Archaic manner
Pentelic marble
Height 1.08 m
Naples Museum, inv. 6808
Found 19 July 1760 in one of the houses
of VIII, 2 or 3 (VIII, 3, 14?)

The goddess is represented striding pur-
posefully forward, bow in hand (the bow
itself being of bronze or wood); she may
also have held some object in her left hand.
The manner of the face and drapery is
consciously derived from Archaic Greek
sculpture, but such features as the move-
ment of the body (involving liberal use of
marble struts), the carving of the hair, the
smoothly polished flesh surfaces, and the
execution of the drapery (with consider-
able use of the drill and with the surfaces
left as worked with a fine, flat chisel) — all
point to it being the work of Athenian
workshops at the turn of the first centuries
B.C./A.D., or slightly later. Such archaizing
work was in great demand in Rome (see
also No. 83), and there were many copyist
workshops both in Greece and in Italy
busy turning out work of this sort.

The statue was found in the garden of
the same house as Nos. 199, 301, 302. It
stood on a base veneered with colored
marbles, within a shrine that was approached by steps and preceded by a pair
of herm shafts in *cipollino* marble. When
found, it still retained many traces of
color: yellow (gilded?) hair; eyes with red-
brown irises and black pupils; black eyelashes and eyebrows; diadem, pink with
yellow rosettes; quiver, pink with white
decoration; pink and yellow, finely detailed border on the drapery; sandals with
pink, yellow, and blue straps; and on the
plinth, traces of black.

PAH I, 114; F. Studniczka, "Die archaische
Artemisstatue aus Pompeji," *RM 3* (1888)
277-302; Reuterswaard, *Polychromie* 184,
note 518; W. Fuchs, *Die Skulpturen der
Griechen* (1969) 241f.

82

83
Statue of the youthful Apollo in the Archaic style
Pentelic marble
Height 1.05 m
Naples Museum, inv. 146103
Found in the House of the Menander
(I, 10, 4) in the northern corridor of the peristyle, near the *tablinum*

The figure of the god, supported by a tree stump and socketed into a rectangular plinth, is accompanied by a griffin. His right hand appears to hold a *plectrum,* which strongly suggests that the left arm (carved in a separate piece of marble and attached with an iron dowel) held a lyre. The front part of the left foot, where it overlaps the plinth, is another added piece, the sculptor having slightly miscalculated the size of the statue in relation to the block of marble. There are clear traces of original coloring: on the eyeballs a faint circle of black for the iris and a large black dot spotted with white for the pupil; reddish brown for the eyebrows; and carmine red for the corners of the mouth. The dirty brown color on the hair is the decayed remains of the substance used as a base for a golden yellow coloring, possibly gilding. The tree stump was bluish gray.

Both the treatment of the head and the rigidly frontal pose derive directly from the conventions of Archaic statuary, but the generally more naturalistic treatment of the body, with the weight resting firmly on the right leg, betrays a knowledge of later, more sophisticated Greek sculptural traditions. Apollo holding or accompanied by a griffin is in any case uncommon in Greek statuary; there does not seem to be any close parallel. This is evidently the eclectic work of Athenian sculptors, producing for the Roman market around the beginning of the first century A.D. and adding the figure of a griffin from the familiar repertory of late Hellenistic decorative motifs. The same workshop may well have produced the Apollo in the Vatican Museums (Chiaramonti 285), of which the dimensions and basic pose are almost identical, but the position of the arms is reversed and the griffin is omitted.

No suitable base was found within the House of the Menander. It has been suggested that the statue originally stood in the Temple of Apollo, and that it was removed temporarily for safe custody during the restorations after the earthquake of A.D. 62.
Maiuri, *Menandro* 410ff.

83

84

84
Head of a youth in the Archaic style
Pentelic marble
Height 28 cm
Naples Museum, inv. 109621
From Pompeii, House VII, 3, 40

The head is that of a youth with his hair
dressed in a style favored by the Greek
aristocracy about 500 B.C. The sharpness
of the detail and the smooth finish on the
face, however, indicate a date around the
beginning of the first century A.D. The
base of the neck is carved for insertion
into a body, perhaps a herm.

The closest parallels to this head are
found on double herms, in association
with the head of a bearded old man with
a similar hairstyle (the forerunner of the
theatrical *onkos*), e.g., Louvre inv. 198.
M. Bieber, *JdAI* 32, 1917, 85; idem,
Theater 24.

85 (color plate, vol. 1, p. 28)
Garden painting: a white stork and lizard and a pet dog
Length 1.30 m, height 55 cm
Naples Museum, inv. 110877
From the House of the Epigrams (V, 1, 18)

The painting, on a black ground and divided into two panels by red lines, stood
in the southeast corner of the peristyle,
where it occupied a position closely resembling that of the very similar paintings
in the peristyle of the House of the Menander, except that in this instance the
screen wall continued upward, occupying
the entire space between the two columns.
On the left is a white stork picking at a
lizard, and on the right a large green
plant; between them, painted over the
vertical red framing line, is the figure of a
small, terrier-like dog, above the head of
which is painted in white, A. SYNCLETVS.
The adjoining panel to the left (Naples
inv. 110876) shows a white stork grappling with a snake.
Bull Inst XLIX (1877) 30.

85

86
Wall painting of a cat
Height 33 cm, width 42 cm
Naples Museum, inv. 8648
From Pompeii

A fragment probably cut from the upper
zone of a late Third Style wall, which
contained Egyptianizing elements. The
cat, painted in silhouette, is shown curled
up on a low upholstered stool.

86

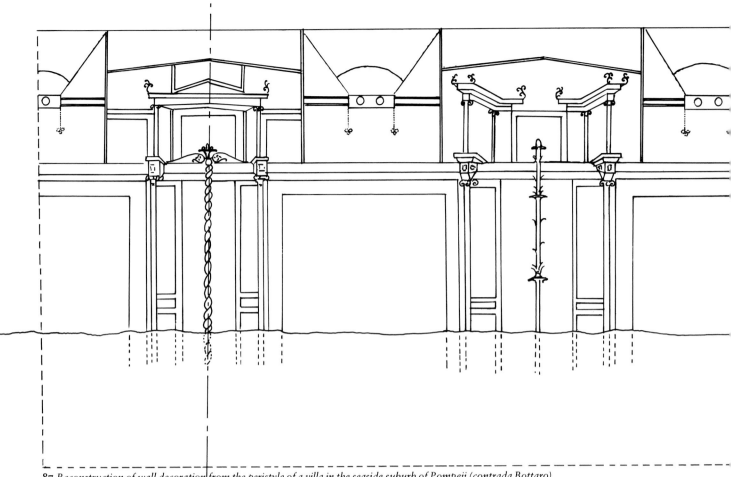

87 Reconstruction of wall decoration from the peristyle of a villa in the seaside suburb of Pompeii (contrada Bottaro)

87 Museum of Fine Arts, 33.506

87 Museum of Fine Arts, 33.497

87 Museum of Fine Arts, 33.496

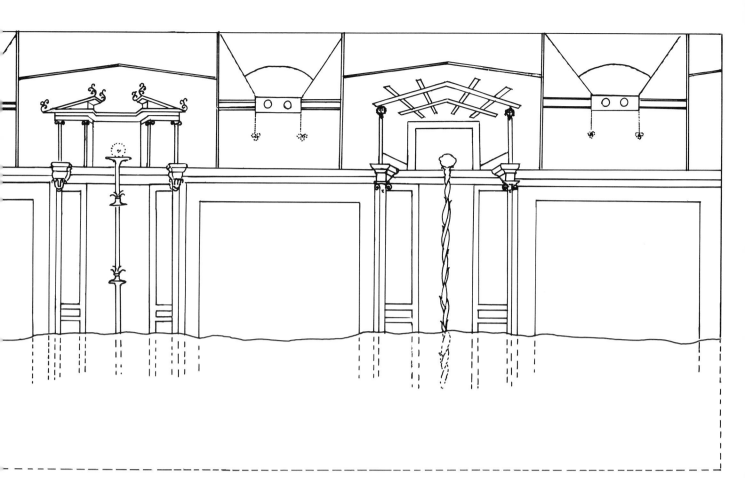

87 *Museum of Fine Arts, 33.498*

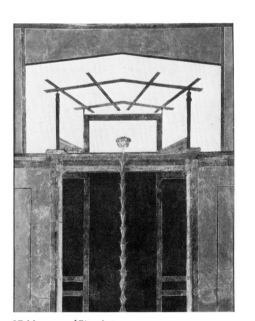

87 *Museum of Fine Arts, 33.500*

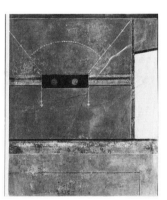

87 *Museum of Fine Arts, 33.501*

87

Decorative wall paintings
Museum of Fine Arts, Boston
Inv. 33.496: height 1.907 m, width 1.465 m
Inv. 33.497: height 2.01 m, width 1.445 m
Inv. 33.498: height 2.052 m, width 1.365 m
Inv. 33.500: height 1.938 m, width 1.393 m
Inv. 33.501: height 1.35 m, width 97.8 cm
Inv. 33.506: height 1.37 m, width 75.2 cm
From the colonnaded courtyard (peristyle) of a villa in the seaside suburb of Pompeii (contrada Bottaro)

The paintings formed the decoration of one side of the courtyard. Simple panels, which were largely destroyed when the paintings were removed from the wall in the first years of this century, alternated with column-framed "niches," which have been almost completely preserved. Another unit from the wall is in the Field Museum in Chicago. The ensemble forms a flat, continuous surface; the niches act as shallow frames for the candelabra that give a decorative focus to each unit. The window-like panels above give the only suggestion of deep space. The paintings may have been executed after the earthquake of A.D. 62, but the designer was still in sympathy with the flat, severe Third Style decoration of the earlier part of the century. His restrained approach may have been influenced by the architectural setting: a long corridor-like space whose main feature was the view out into a garden filled with elegantly made sculpture. A seated bronze Hercules, now in the Naples Museum, and several small, decorative marble sculptures were found in the excavation.

NSc 1902, 572ff.; L. D. Caskey, *BMFA* XXXVII (1939) 9-16; cf. H. F. De Cou, *Antiquities from Boscoreale in Field Museum of Natural History* (Chicago 1912) pl. CXXVIII, no. 24672.

88

Wall painting: the Judgment of Solomon
Width 1.60 m, height 65 cm
Naples Museum, inv. 113197
From the House of the Doctor (VIII, 5, 24)

Pygmies enact what appears to be the well-known story of King Solomon giving judgment in a case where two women disputed the ownership of a child. Solomon is shown bearded, seated on a raised dais (*tribunal*) between two counselors, with a bodyguard of armed soldiers. Before him the true mother kneels and pleads for her child's life, while the false mother watches with apparent indifference as a soldier prepares to cut it in half. The scene is one of three matching panels that were painted on the parapet wall surrounding a miniature garden peristyle, the other two being Egyptianizing landscapes, one with pygmies fighting off crocodiles and hippopotami, the other with pygmies banqueting beneath a large awning slung from trees (No. 89).

Pygmies portrayed in Egyptianizing settings are one of the commonplaces of Roman Imperial art. Because of the strong element of caricature, this picture can hardly be ascribed to direct Jewish influence in Pompeii, although there were unquestionably many Jews settled in Campania. If correctly identified, it is, rather, evidence at second hand of the strong influence of the very large Jewish community in Alexandria. An alternative possibility is that the picture represents an older, native Egyptian version of some traditional story of royal wisdom, such as that attributed to King Bocchoris.

NSc 1882, 322-323; G. Gatti, "Il Giudizio di Salomone in un dipinto pompeiano," in *Rivista Antimassonica* IV, 1898; Lumbroso, *RendLinc* ser. III, 11, 1882-83, 303-305; J. Gutmann, *Antike Kunst* 15, 1972, 122-124.

89

Wall painting: pygmies in a Nilotic landscape
Height 60 cm, width 220 cm
Naples Museum, inv. 113196
From the House of the Doctor (VIII, 5, 24)

Pygmies are shown engaging in the ridiculous activities normally attributed to them in ancient art. A pygmy attacks an ibis and is restrained. Another pygmy is being swallowed by a hippopotamus in spite of the efforts of two friends to save him. Banqueting pygmies watch indecent entertainment.

Such scenes provide evidence for contact between the ancient Mediterranean and central Africa, but they also show how indirect that contact was. Already in Archaic Greek art, pygmies were shown in battle with birds (cranes), and subsequent embellishments are dictated more by humorous fantasy than by any direct experience. In Hellenistic times the pygmies were thought of as localized in the Nile valley since the Nile formed the principal line of contact between central Africa and the Mediterranean.

NSc 1882, 322-323; J. Marcadé, *Roma Amor* (New York 1961) 46; cf. *EAA*, s. v. *Pigmei*; J. Leclant, in *The Image of the Black in Western Art* I (New York 1976) 269-273; Schefold, *Vergessenes Pompeii* 77f., 151, 154-155, pl. 144,2

88

89

IV The House

The poet Menander

90 (not illus.)
Model of the House of the Menander
(1, 10, 4)
Scale 1:25
Lent by Imperial Tobacco Limited

The House of the Menander, which takes its name from a portrait of the poet painted on the walls of an *exedra* opening off the peristyle, occupies the greater part of an insula situated in the heart of the residential quarter that lies to the east of the Via Stabiana and to the south of the Via dell' Abbondanza. A seal found in the quarters of the steward bearing the name of Eros, the freedman or trusted slave of a certain Quintus Poppaeus, tells us that at the time of the eruption the house belonged to a member of the prosperous local family of the Poppaei, the family of which Nero's wife, Poppaea Sabina, was a member and to which the Villa at Oplontis probably belonged. It was excavated by Maiuri from 1927 to 1932.

The site had a long and varied history. At this point the ground slopes quite sharply southward toward the river Sarno, and although only further excavation could determine its earlier history in any detail, the plan and the masonry still upstanding tell us quite a bit of the story. The earliest visible remains date from the second half of the third century B.C., at which time the insula was subdivided into a number of small houses, of which five faced north along the northern frontage. The rest seem to have followed the line of the slope, at least three facing east and two more facing west, of which one, the House of the Lovers at the southwest angle, still retained its separate identity in A.D. 79. Three rooms of one of these early houses, with remains of First Style wall painting, were found by Maiuri when relaying the floor of the large *triclinium* (Room 18) off the east wing of the later peristyle. The early floors were about six feet deeper than those of the later building, and the walls several degrees out of alignment with it. At this early period the House of the Menander probably consisted simply of the atrium with, probably, a garden plot behind it.

Some time in the second century B.C., this nucleus was modernized and enlarged, with a handsome new façade and the insertion of the Corinthian columns flanking the entrance to the *tablinum*, together with a formalization of the garden area beyond, to which belonged the three central columns of the north wing of the later peristyle. Then, shortly after the middle of the first century B.C., came another and more radical development. The old buildings around the atrium were again partly modernized, but the main living quarters were transferred to a new setting around a large rectangular peristyle. To create this, several of the adjoining properties were bought up, and place was made for the peristyle by terracing upward and outward across the middle of the insula, leaving only the servants' quarters at the old level. A series of handsome living rooms (14-18) was added along the east side and a bath suite along the southern part of the west side. The old *tablinum* and the rooms to right and left of it now opened southward onto the north side of the peristyle. The south side, where the terracing did not allow for rooms, was modeled into a series of decorative *exedrae*. With the subsequent purchase of the property at the southeast corner of the insula for conversion into farm quarters, the house occupied the whole insula except for the House of the Lovers and the buildings at the northeast and northwest corners.

As everywhere else in Pompeii, the earthquake of A.D. 62 did serious damage here. In A.D. 79 the atrium area, which had been redecorated in the early Fourth Style manner shortly before the earthquake, was still awaiting restoration, and many of the rooms were found unfurnished; and although work was in progress in the peristyle area and by A.D. 79 had been nearly completed (only the baths still retain their Second Style ornament), the family had not yet resumed residence. As in the Villa of the Mysteries and at Oplontis, the property was left in the charge of the steward, Eros, who continued to operate the agricultural side of the estate, which may very well have consisted of vineyards and market gardens situated in the belt of substantially open ground that lay immediately to the south, inside the walls between the Stabian Gate and the Palaestra. Except for their positions inside and outside the walls respectively, the House of the Menander and the Villa of the Mysteries in this respect had a great deal in common.

Space does not permit a room-by-room account of the decoration of the house. The wall painting offers a fine range of Fourth Style work, some of it (in the atrium area) painted before the earthquake of A.D. 62, most of it (in the peristyle and the rooms opening off it) in the later post-earthquake phase. Of the Second Style paintings, which once adorned the whole of the peristyle area, one can now catch some tantalizing glimpses in the bath suite, notably in the apse of the hot room (*caldarium*) with its frieze of black and white figured panels simulating stuccoed niches and, above it, a second frieze with three polychrome scenes of women bathing; but most of this earlier work had been ruthlessly stripped off by the Fourth Style decorators. They were, on the other hand, glad to retain the fine mosaic pavements of the earlier period. These include a splendid polychrome Nilotic panel in the "Green Room" (11) with pygmies and boats in a landscape of river birds, plants, and architectural scenery (see page 109) set in a severely simple black and white surround; a sadly damaged panel of a satyr and nymph in a double *cubiculum* (Room 21), which in the last period appears to have been converted into a library; and the fine series of pavements in the bath suite. The last-named in particular illustrate the art of decorative paving at a turning point in its Roman development: those of the *caldarium* and of the *apodyterium* still strongly influenced by the sort of Hellenistic work one finds on Delos, whereas that of the corridor between them, portraying four strigils, an oil flask, and a Negro slave bearing two *askoi*, clearly foreshadows the "popular" Italic style of the skeleton mosaic (No. 109). The floor of the atrium vestibule is a fine example of a pavement made entirely of fragments of colored marble set in a ground of black tesserae.

Of the individual rooms we can only mention Room 4, a symmetrical early Fourth Style scheme incorporating three lively panel pictures with scenes from the Trojan War; the "Green Room" (11) at the northwest corner of the peristyle, a fine example of the sort of late Fourth Style work that tends to refer back to earlier styles and motifs, including a frieze, 25 cm high, portraying in white on red the rape of the Lapith women by the Centaurs, a rare survival of a type of figured frieze that was common in the late Hellenistic world; and the large *triclinium* (Room 18), which exemplifies another trend in late Fourth Style painting, one that relied for its effect on the contraposition and repetition of broad sheets of color, picked out with dainty decorative detail and small, isolated figures. Along the south side of the peristyle are two semi-circular *exedrae* (22 and 24) illustrated Diana hunting (22) and a rustic shrine with an image of Venus (24), both displayed within spacious landscape settings; while the central, rectangular *exedra* (23), the focus of the whole architectural scheme, contained figures of three of the great dramatic poets of the past, or of two of them flanking a central figure of Dionysus. Sadly, two figures are now unrecognizable, but the third, on the right-hand wall, is the seated Menander from whom the house takes its name.

Other features of note are the traces of a wooden screen, 2.10 m high, set across the opening between the *tablinum* and the atrium, and of a curtain across the entrance to Room 4; the terracotta surround of the *compluvium* (the opening in the roof); the gabled *lararium* in the atrium, on the right-hand side on entering; and a second household shrine at the southwest corner of the peristyle. This last, in a room decorated with Second Style paintings that may have been retained in the last period as a mark of respect for tradition, consists of a rectangular altar of masonry set in front of a recess, in which were displayed one small seated figure and four small heads or busts, made of wood or of wax, the *imagines maiorum*, symbolic images of the family ancestors (see page 108). Of more specifically architectural interest are the extreme irregularity of the peristyle colonnades, with the columns spaced so as

to give the maximum visibility outward from the principal living rooms, regardless of the architectural proprieties; the lighting of the great *triclinium* (Room 18) by means of a window set high in the walls, above the adjoining roofs (remains of a window frame were found among the masonry fallen from the gable); and the traces of a wooden, open-air *triclinium* beneath a wooden pavilion in the center of the peristyle garden, as in the House of P. Paquius Proculus (II, 7, 1).

At its greatest extent the residence occupied the whole of the center of the insula, terraced out at a level corresponding to that of the atrium and of the main entrance in the middle of the north side. Built around and up against this terraced area were the service quarters. To the west of the peristyle, beyond the baths at the end of a long corridor, lay the kitchen, a small vegetable garden, and some storerooms. On this side there was no access from the street. To the east, along the street frontage, there were more storerooms, and at an upper level, the quarters of the domestic staff. Alongside this block, at the north end of it, was the steward's lodging, and at the south end, occupying the southeast corner of the insula, were the stables and farm buildings.

The kitchen block (Rooms 26-28) was by any modern standards impossibly remote from the *triclinium* where the food was served, but this does not seem to have worried a Roman householder—what were slaves for, after all? From the corridor, steps led down into an enclosed courtyard at the old ground level, which was used as a vegetable garden. Along the east side of it lay four basement rooms, which constituted the substructures of the bath building. In one of them, under the *caldarium* (and helping to heat it) there was a large bread oven, and the other three were used as storerooms. It was here, securely protected from recovery after the eruption, that the excavators found the remains of two large chests and their contents. One of these had contained jewelry and the family store of ready cash, forty-six gold and silver coins to a total value of 1,432 sestertii together with a collection of family silver, 118 pieces in all, weighing a total of just under 53 lb (24 kg). Many of them were handsomely decorated and included a number of antique pieces. The only comparable find from the Vesuvius area is the Boscoreale treasure (see page 108).

The slaves' quarters, which were accessible from the residence only by a narrow, sloping corridor at the southeast corner of the peristyle, call for little special comment. They had a small independent kitchen and a lavatory. A group of bodies found at the foot of the stairs to the upper story (between Rooms 19 and 21), one of them carrying a lantern identical to No. 163, are now thought to be those of workmen overcome while engaged in a salvage

operation after the eruption. Most of the staff, it seems, got away in time. The steward Eros, on the other hand, died at his post, stretched out on his bedstead in Room 43. This was the living room of a small separate house, with its own entrance leading into a substantial atrium (41) and, beyond it, a tiny garden courtyard (44) with a private kitchen and lavatory. In the steward's room were found his signet ring; a leather purse containing his savings, ninety coins totaling 527 sestertii; some fine bronze vessels; and a large number of iron tools (including fifteen vine-pruning knives) for issue to the farmworkers.

The farm quarters were built around three sides of a courtyard (34) with a wide entrance from the street. Along the north side there was an open lean-to gallery, in which were found the remains of a two-wheeled cart. The far end was occupied by stabling for four animals, together with a cistern and a drinking trough (29, 30), and along the south side were storerooms, a lavatory, and a wooden stair up to the farmworkers' quarters (31, 32). The corner of the block, always a valuable property, was let out independently as a bar (*thermopolium*), as was also a single-roomed shop facing onto the street to the south. Although the farm property evidently included vines, it did not press its own wine (as did the Villa of the Mysteries). There was no press, and a stack of forty-three amphoras were all empties awaiting disposal.

The two houses at the northwest corner of the insula both date back to the third century B.C., one of them still retaining traces of its First Style painting. Both ceased to be residences after A.D. 62. One became a weaving establishment, the other the workshop of a smith who also practiced carpentry. The miniature two-story apartment in the angle between the latter and the House of the Menander was, as the *graffiti* make very clear, the lodging of a group of popular call-girls. The houses at the northeast corner, too, seem to have been taken over in this last period for commercial or industrial use, including a cookshop (*caupona*). Thanks to a lively exchange of *graffiti*, we even know the name of the barmaid, Iris, one of whose boyfriends was a weaver from down the street. In the last period before the eruption this was evidently still a lively quarter, but socially it had come down in the world.

One final *graffito* was found just outside the front door of the steward's quarters. It tells the traveler where to find company at Nuceria: *Nucerea quaeres ad porta[m] Romana[m] in vico venerio Novelliam Primigeniam* ("At Nuceria ask for Novellia Primigenia, in the street of Venus near the Rome Gate").

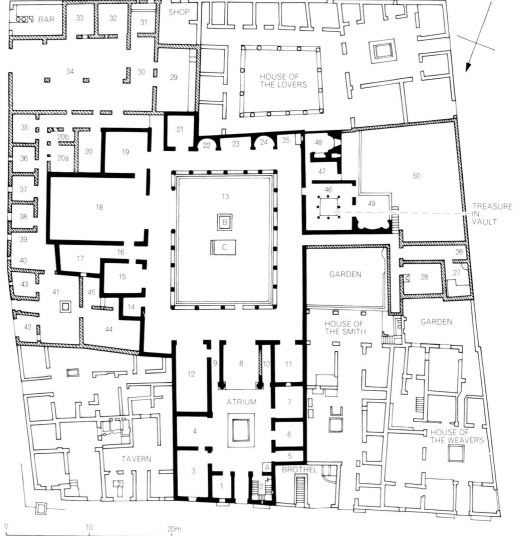

1. Door keeper's lodge
2. Staircase to upper floor
3. Bedroom later used as workshop
4. "Ala"
5. Storeroom
6-7. Bedrooms
8. Tablinum
9. Corridor
10. Cupboard
11. Green oecus
12. Large exedra
13. Peristyle garden
14. Store
15. Red oecus
16. Corridor
17. Bedroom
18. Dining room (triclinium)
19. Yellow oecus
20. 35-40. Servants' quarters
21. Day bedroom/library
22-24. Exedrae
25. Exedra with imagines maiorum
26-28. Kitchens
29. Stable
30-34. Farm quarters
41-45. Steward's lodging
43. Bedroom
44. Garden
46. Vestibule to bath suite
47. Warm undressing room
   (apodyterium)
48. Hot room (caldarium)
49. Sun terrace
50. Kitchen garden
A. Household shrine (lararium)
B. Fountain basin
C. Wooden dining area
   (triclinium)

BAR 33 32 31 SHOP

HOUSE OF THE LOVERS

34 30 29

35 20b

36 20a 20 19

37 18

38

39

40 17 16

43 41 45 15

42 44 14

13

B

C

22 23 24 25 48

47

46 49 50

TREASURE IN VAULT

GARDEN

26

28 27

HOUSE OF THE SMITH

GARDEN

12 9 8 10 11

7

ATRIUM

4 6

5

3 A BROTHEL

1 2

TAVERN

HOUSE OF THE WEAVERS

0   10   20m

91

93

92

91
Bronze figure of an old donkey
Length 12 cm, height 9 cm
Naples Museum, inv. 4955
From one of the sites in the Vesuvius area

Hollow cast and carefully worked over after casting to give the effect of coarse hair. A square hole in the belly suggests that the figure was attached to some larger object as a handle or decorative finial.

92
Bronze figurine of a deer
Length 28 cm, height 30 cm
Naples Museum, old inv. 2134 (base, 109992)
From one of the sites in the Vesuvius area

Hollow cast in two halves, the body is engraved with a delicate flower design that serves to mask the joint. Although the alabaster on which it stands is ancient, it does not belong; but the figure does seem, rather unusually, to have been a purely decorative piece.
Cf. De Ridder, *Bronzes antiques du Louvre* (1913), no. 196.

93
Statuette of a Placentarius in gilded bronze and silver
Height 25.4 cm
Naples Museum, inv. 143759
From the House of the Ephebe (I, 7, 10-12)

One of a group of four identical figures found together in a wooden box in a room off the atrium. The figure is bronze and the tray and base silver. They are usually thought to represent *placentarii* (sellers of *placentae;* see Cato, *De Re Rustica,* 76), itinerant piemen crying their wares. The element of caricature is typical of late Hellenistic art. Equally typical of Roman taste is the adaptation of a *genre* type to a functional purpose. These were probably pieces for the service of some special delicacy.
Maiuri, *BdA* 1925, 268-275.

94 (withdrawn from exhibition)
Terracotta toad with traces of blue-green glaze
Naples Museum, inv. 76/166

95
One-handled glass cup
Height 14.3 cm, upper diameter 13.8 cm
Naples Museum, inv. 11961
From Pompeii

The glass is yellowish green. Five lines have been incised below the handle. This kind of cup imitates prototypes in metal-work like the silver cup decorated with ivy leaves, No. 324.
Isings 52, form 37.

96
Tall glass beaker with molded decoration
Height 14.4 cm
Naples Museum, inv. 12279
From Pompeii

The greenish glass is densely ornamented with bands of relief decoration. The bands comprise, from top to bottom, a row of bosses, an ivy vine, a maeander separating scallop shells, "tear drops" and ovoids, and a laurel wreath. Faint vertical ridges reflect the join between the two halves of the mold.
Isings 45, form 31.

95

96

97

99

100

101

98

97
Small bulbous glass jug
Height 12.2 cm, diameter of body 7.8 cm
Naples Museum, inv. 109423
From the atrium of House VII, 7, 13 (?),
11 January 1872

An imitation of a fine metal form, free-
blown, with short raised ribs running up
from the base. The attachment of the
handle to the rim is decorated with im-
pressed ridges.
Isings 76, form 57.

98 (color plate, vol. 1, p. 30)
Stemmed goblet in cobalt blue glass
Height 14 cm, diameter of rim 15.4 cm
Naples Museum, inv. 76/215
From one of the sites in the Vesuvius area

The body was blown into a mold; two
horizontal wheel-cut lines decorate the
outside. The stem is formed from two
large beads of glass and the foot added
separately. Such drinking cups were used
at table; for a silver version see No. 246.
Isings 50, form 36a.

99 (color plate, vol. 1, p. 30)
Ribbed blue glass bowl
Height 8.9 cm, diameter 18.9 cm
Naples Museum, inv. 13810
From Pompeii

These bowls were made by pressing soft
glass into a mold; the interior was polished on a wheel, the exterior by a second,
brief exposure to fire. Bowls of this form,
in multi-colored as well as in monochrome glass, were popular in the first
century A.D.
Harden, *Camulodunum* 301ff.

100 (color plate, vol. 1, p. 29)
Small blue glass jug (askos)
Height 11 cm, length 21.1 cm
Naples Museum, inv. 109433
From Pompeii, House IX, 2, 26

The glass-blower has imitated a shape
long familiar in Greek pottery and in
Campanian bronze ware. These *askoi* are
commonly found in pairs and were evidently so used; they are often very finely
worked, being blown into a mold rather
than free-blown, as is this example. Mid-
first century A.D.
Isings 77, form 59.

101 (color plate, vol. 1, p. 29)
**Small jug (askos) in black and white
marbled glass**
Height 9.5 cm, length 13.4 cm
Naples Museum, inv. 118143
From Pompeii, in IX, 7, 6

Like No. 100 this is free-blown, but it is
squatter in shape and made in thicker,
opaque glass. It was found in 1888, together with three other *askoi* in an
aedicula opposite the entrance to IX, 7, 6;
altogether 23 pieces of glass, some of
them colored, were found in this building.
Brightly variegated glass in strong colors
was very popular in the early stages of
Roman glass production. Late first century B.C. to early first century A.D.
Isings 77, form 59.

102
Shallow two-handled glass cup
Height 3.8 cm, diameter 12.6 cm
Naples Museum, inv. 133273
From Pompeii, from the *tablinum* of VI, 16, 28

One of a pair of identical cups, mold-blown with formal decoration in relief. Second half of the first century A.D.
NSc 1908, 277.

103
Long-necked glass flask
Height 15 cm
Naples Museum, inv. 12435
From Pompeii

The form is free-blown, decorated with thin threads of glass trailed over the bulbous body as ribs. Such flasks are very common at Pompeii, though usually undecorated, and were used for serving liquids or for oils used in bathing, as was the bronze example, No. 221. Inside the flask is a quantity of black powder, the decayed remains of its contents. Early first century A.D.
Isings 34, form 16.

104 (color plate, vol. 1, p. 30)
Dark blue glass jug
Height 18 cm
Naples Museum, inv. 13539
From Pompeii

Fine-quality work, free-blown with a drawn-out spout and an applied handle. The form clearly imitates that of a bronze vessel.
Isings 71, form 54.

104

105

102

103

105
Large glass dish
Height 3.5 cm, diameter 22.3 cm
Naples Museum, inv. 11588
From Pompeii

Blown into a mold. A large dish of the same kind, filled with fruit, is shown in a Fourth Style still life painting from Pompeii (Naples Museum, inv. 8645). The form is copied from *terra sigillata* pottery.
Isings 39, form 23; cf. Beyen pl. VIII.

106
Fragment of a Second Style wall painting
Height 1.18 m, width 60 cm
Naples Museum, inv. 9847
From the Villa of Diomedes, Pompeii, 1772

The scheme to which this fragment belonged was divided into three main panels by four fluted columns. Between the outer pairs of columns ran a tall screen wall, over the top of which could be glimpsed a receding architectural perspective. A *tholos* occupied the middle of the central intercolumniation. The fragment formed part of the right-hand panel and shows part of one column and of the red screen wall. Hanging against the latter is shown a dead hare and, placed on top of it, the mask of an old father in Greek New Comedy. To the right of it is part of a column shown in perspective beyond the screen wall. Naples Museum, inv. 8594 comes from a similar wall in the same room (see drawing).
Curtius, figs. 74-76; Webster, *New Comedy* 185, NP 3.

107
Wall painting of a silver wine bucket (situla)
Height 77 cm, width 41 cm
Naples Museum, inv. 9965
From the peristyle wall in the Villa of Publius Fannius Synistor at Boscoreale

This *situla* is one of several objects, mostly prizes for athletics, shown as if placed on a dado in front of the painted screen wall of a Second Style scheme. It stands on three low feet in the form of animal's legs, and from the rim spring two tall, ornate handle mounts. Placed diagonally behind it is a trident entwined with a snake.
P. W. Lehmann, *Roman Wall Paintings from Boscoreale* (Cambridge, Mass. 1953) 11f.

106

107

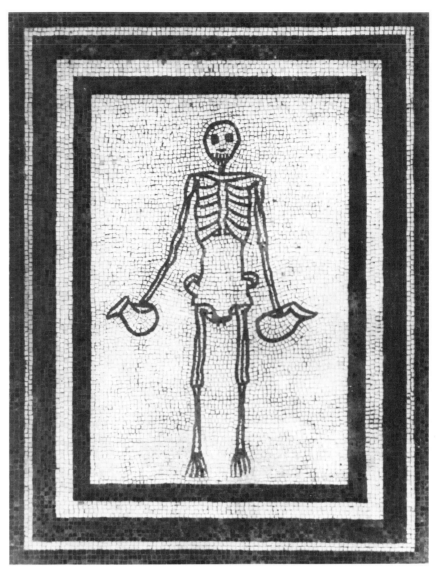

109

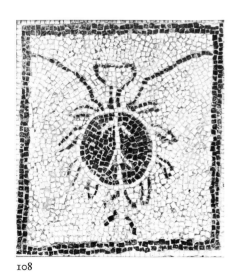

108

108
Mosaic representing a crab or spider
Width 41 cm, height 45 cm
Pompeii, Storerooms, inv. 13933
From House VI, 15, 3

This naive portrayal of some indeterminate crustacean or spider-like creature represents the opposite extreme of competence and artistic intent to the sophisticated late Hellenistic school of craftsmanship exemplified by Nos. 238, 305. The work of some local craftsman used to laying simple black and white geometrical patterns, it would have been displayed in the middle of a much larger area of white tesserae. Like similar mosaics portraying animals and other symbolic figures, it would have been placed near the entrance to avert ill luck.

109
Mosaic representing a skeleton carrying two askoi
Height 91 cm, width 70 cm
Naples Museum, inv. 9978
From one of the sites in the Vesuvius area

The skeleton, set within a rectangular frame and carried out in black and white mosaic, holds a pair of wine jugs (*askoi*). A product of the *memento mori* conventions fostered by Epicurean philosophy, it probably adorned the center of a *triclinium*. Unlike the colored floor mosaics, which derive from Hellenistic models, these black and white mosaics were a specifically Italian creation. Often naive, but always direct and lively, they are the artistic equivalent of the "popular" strain in contemporary painting.

110

111

110
Tall bronze bowl
Height 33.7 cm, diameter of rim 31 cm
Naples Museum, inv. 73146
From Herculaneum

The bowl, which has a molded foot and a frieze of molded ornament below the rim, has two identical applied handles. Early publications show it as standing on a graceful molded pedestal, about 23 cm high, with three animal's-paw feet, but this has become separated and appears now to be lost. The handles portray two trousered barbarians, molded in the round, fighting, with their lozenge-shaped shields locked between them. They stand upon and are attached to the body of the bowl by a calyx-shaped escutcheon, on which are displayed a pair of crossed spears and two similar shields. At the base of the calyx is an ox-skull (*bukranion*), a common decorative motif in late Hellenistic work of all sorts. Barbarian shields, in this case oval, are the principal motif also of the frieze on the body of the bowl.

The same earlier publications speak of this piece as a trophy awarded for victory in gladiatorial combat, and the pedestal, to which it appears to have been fastened by a rivet, would indeed suggest some form of ceremonial use. But if these are gladiatorial combatants, they represent an earlier stage of gladiatorial history than the sophisticated, stylized gladiatorial combat of Imperial times, to which alone such trophies would have been appropriate. Barbarians, and in particular Gauls, were one of the commonplaces of Hellenistic art, and pairs of figures fighting were one of the stock themes of Capuan bronzework. From its shape this piece could well be as early as the second century B.C.

MB VIII (Naples 1832) pl. xv; Ceci VI, no. 37.

111 (color plate, vol. I, p. 24)
Landscape panel of a rustic sanctuary
Height 34 cm, length 61 cm
Naples Museum, inv. 9419
From Herculaneum

Against the white ground of a lateral panel in a Third Style scheme is a picture framed in red, mounted on a slender support. On a rocky outcrop is a small shrine, behind which is a walled garden with two columns capped with urns and a large tree. In front of the sanctuary is another column, tied with a garland and supporting a tripod. In the distance are two figures carrying bundles, and the faint outline of another building.

Rostowzew, "Architekturlandschaft" 84, fig. 50.

112a
Bronze adjustable candelabrum (lamp stand)
Height from 87.2 cm minimum to 138.4 cm maximum
Naples Museum, inv. 111228
From Herculaneum

This lamp stand is made in three pieces. The base, which can be removed, has three legs, ending in bull's feet, which arch outward from beneath a plate decorated with three projecting scallop shells and sea monsters in the form of dogs' heads with pectoral fins. On the base rests a hollow shaft, square in section, topped with a small double herm of a satyr and maenad supporting a *calathus*. The upper part consists of a square rod that fits into and is free to move within the shaft, and that carries the actual lamp support, in the form of a vase. The height of the stand could be adjusted by fitting a small bronze pin, chained to the underside of the satyr's left "arm," into one of a series of holes spaced down the length of the movable rod.

This piece is one of a group, of which the detail of the little herms and of the bases varies considerably, but of which the technical features are so closely related throughout that they are almost certainly the product of a single workshop. About the end of the first century B.C.

Chiurazzi no. 469.

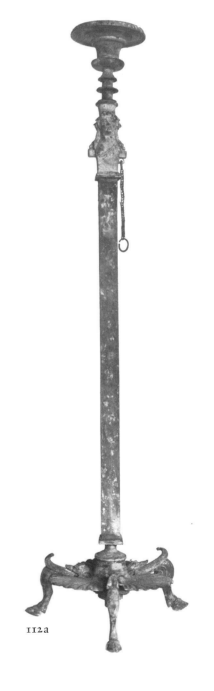

112a

112b

112b
Bronze oil lamp
Diameter 9.7 cm, length 14.1 cm
Naples Museum, inv. 72435
Probably from Pompeii or Herculaneum

The lamp bears a striking similarity to terracotta lamps with plain nozzles of the later first century A.D. The higher-quality metal piece, however, has the added features of a leaf-decorated handle and a lid to close the filler hole. The chain is fastened to the lid and handle with modern wire loops.
Cf. H. Menzel, *Antike Lampen* (Mainz 1969) 49ff., nos. 303, 307, 308.

113
Table support (trapezophorus) with a figure of Attis
Gray and white Italian marble
Height 83 cm
Naples Museum, inv. 120425
From the atrium of House no. 78 on the Via Stabiana, found 3 March 1866

Tables of bronze or marble, set against a wall and supported on a single leg, are a common feature of Pompeian house furniture. To the column of marble, which constitutes the actual support, is often added carved decoration, and colored marbles were popular. Although the commonest motifs are Dionysiac, the use of a figure of Attis, as here, is by no means uncommon. Identical pieces have been found at Herculaneum and Capua.

Attis, beloved by Cybele, the Great Goddess of Asia Minor, was a beautiful youth whose self-castration, death, and transformation into a pine tree was the subject of the wild rites of annual mourning associated with her cult. He is here portrayed as a shepherd boy, in oriental dress and wearing a Phrygian cap.
Tran tam Tinh (1975) 283; M. J. Vermaseren, *The Legend of Attis in Greek and Roman Art* (Leiden 1966) 14.

114 (color plate, vol. I, p. 23)
Wall painting: Pan and the nymphs
Height 1.22 m, width 93 cm
Naples Museum, inv. 111473
From the left-hand wall of the same *cubiculum* in the House of Jason as No. 129

Third Style panel showing Pan, pipes in hand, seated on a rock with a goat at his feet. To the left are seated two nymphs, one of them holding two reed pipes in her hand, while to the right another stands playing a lyre *(cithara)*. Beyond the left-hand nymphs is a building set in a rocky landscape, central to which is a pine tree, sacred to Pan.
Schefold, *WP* 265; Peters 97.

115-126 (color plate of nos. 115, 116, vol. I, pp. 26-27)
Decorative wall paintings
From Room 15 *(cubiculum)* in the Villa of Agrippa Postumus at Boscotrecase
115-116 Naples Museum, inv. 138992, 138993: height 2.00 m, width 44 cm
117-126 Metropolitan Museum of Art
(withdrawn from exhibition)
117, inv. 20.192.1: height 2.441 m, width 1.251 m
118, inv. 20.192.2: height 2.445 m, width 0.591 m
119, inv. 20.192.3: height 2.435 m, width 0.606 m
120, inv. 20.192.4: height 2.041 m, width 0.390 m
121, inv. 20.192.5: height 1.861 m, width 0.559 m

113

114

122, inv. 20.192.6: height 1.994 m, width 0.567 m
123, inv. 20.192.7: height 1.854 m, width 0.581 m
124, inv. 20.192.8: height 1.032 m, width 0.302 m
125, inv. 20.192.10: height 0.371 m, width 0.375 m
126, inv. 20.192.11: height 0.390 m, width 0.832 m

The country villa of Boscotrecase, near Pompeii, was discovered in 1902 during the building of a railway. Paintings from four of its *cubicula* were salvaged in the excavations of 1903-1905. In 1906 a new eruption of Vesuvius covered the site.

The brilliant, innovative wall paintings were done for a patron from the highest level of Roman society. Epigraphical evidence from Boscotrecase indicates that the villa belonged to Agrippa Postumus, grandson of Augustus and son of Augustus' most trusted advisor, Agrippa. The villa was probably begun for the elder Agrippa, but the paintings were part of a project carried out around 11 B.C., after Agrippa Postumus had inherited it.

Room 15 has a red dado and walls of polished carbon black. Elongated decorative elements—tripods, candelabra, reed-like colonnettes—divide the walls into panels, on which tiny, unframed landscapes float in what seems to be a nocturnal blackness. The ornamental details are minute, fanciful, exquisite. Many evoke the fabled world of Pharaonic Egypt. There are lotus buds, falcons, and miniature vignettes of exotic pseudo-Egyptian cult ceremonies. Other elements, the paired swans and the griffins, have nothing to do with the Nile. On the North Wall, a roof of the central *aedicula* rests on disc-shaped supports painted with portrait-like profile heads. Fragments of Room 15, divided between Naples and New York, have been reunited for the first time in Boston.
Blanckenhagen and Alexander, *Boscotrecase* pls. 1-9, color pls. A, B.

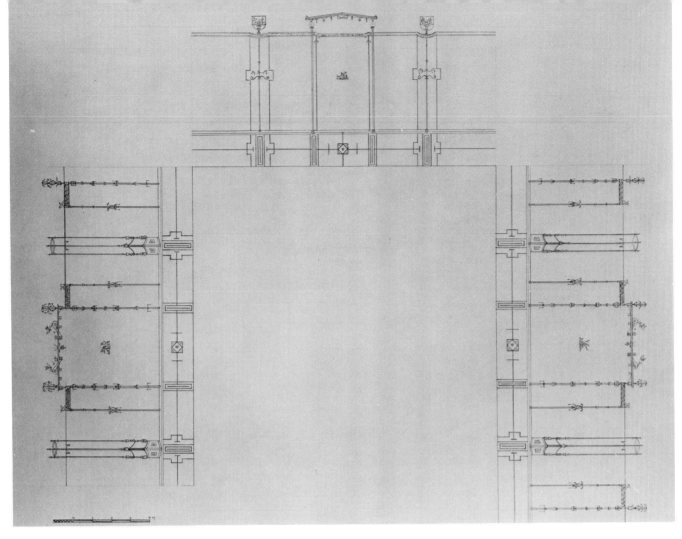

117–126 *Reconstruction of decorative scheme of west, north, and east walls of Room 15 in the Villa of Agrippa Postumus*

West Wall

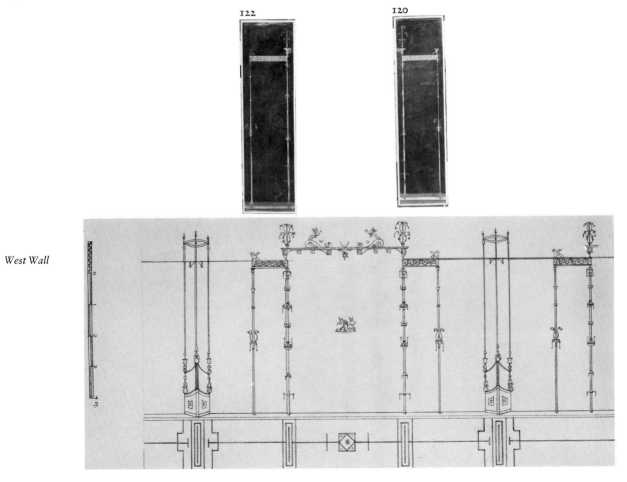

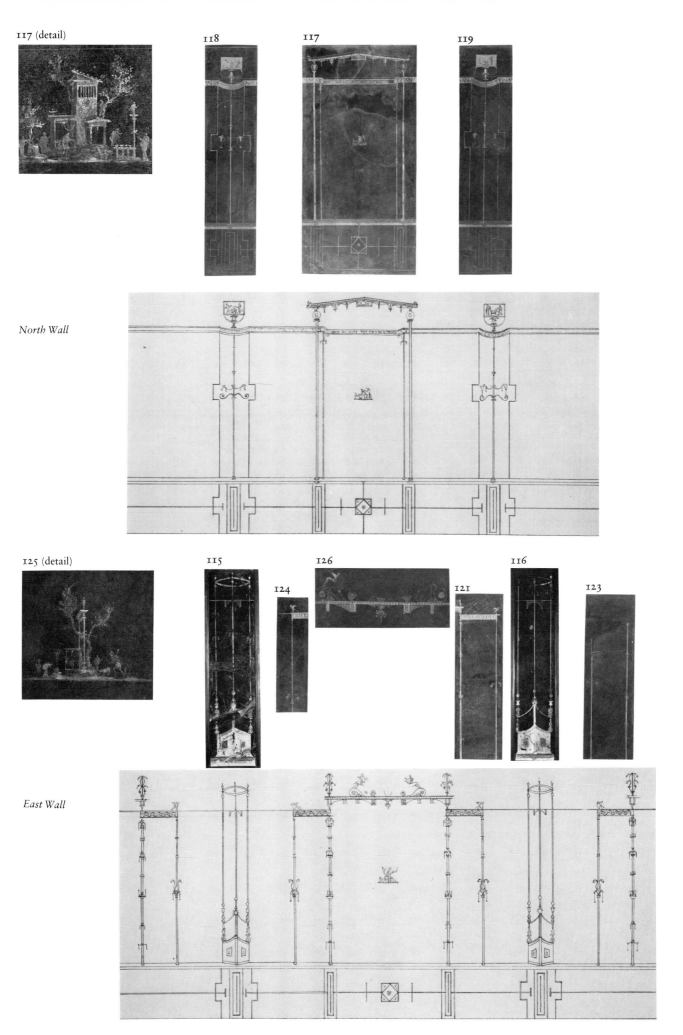

117 (detail)

118   117   119

North Wall

125 (detail)

115   124   126   121   116   123

East Wall

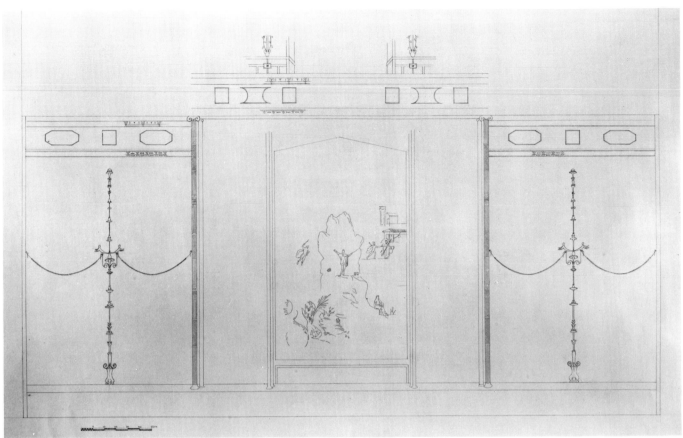

128 *Reconstruction of the East Wall of Room 19 in the Villa of Agrippa Postumus*

127

128

127, 128 (withdrawn from exhibition)
Wall painting: Polyphemus and Galatea
Height 198.12 cm, width 130.81 cm
Metropolitan Museum of Art, inv.
20.192.17
From the West Wall of Room 19 *(cubiculum)* in the Villa of Agrippa Postumus at Boscotrecase

Wall painting: Perseus and Andromeda
Height 198.12 cm, width 129.54 cm
Metropolitan Museum of Art, inv.
20.192.16
From the East Wall of Room 19 *(cubiculum)* in the Villa of Agrippa Postumus at Boscotrecase

Two mythological panels come from facing walls of a room that had Third Style architectural decoration, surviving in fragments, on a red ground. Each myth is set in a landscape whose axis is a craggy, improbably vertical pinnacle of rock. Sea laps about its base, merging in a horizonless unity with the misty sky beyond. Figures are dotted about without regard to consistencies of distance and scale. Polyphemus is the central figure of one panel; the outsize lover gazes longingly with his single eye at Galatea, the sea nymph with whom he is infatuated. His flock of goats grazes near a statue on a tall pedestal. Far away, another figure of Polyphemus acts out a later part of the brute's sad history, hurling a rock after the departing ship of Odysseus, who has blinded him.

The complementary panel illustrates the virtuous, happy love of Perseus and Andromeda. The princess is chained to the cliff; in the foreground the sea monster, come to devour her, lifts his terrifying head from the water. A little Perseus flies in on winged sandals to rescue the girl, attacking from high above, while a female figure, perhaps a personification, perhaps Andromeda's mother, sits mournfully at one side. A second Perseus participates in a sequel episode shown at the upper right. Returning triumphant, the hero is welcomed by Andromeda's father, King Kepheus, and his retinue in front of palatial buildings.
Blanckenhagen and Alexander, *Boscotrecase* pls. 40-46, color pl. D.

129 (color plate, vol. I, p. 21).
Wall painting: Europa riding the bull
Width 99 cm, height 1.25 m
Naples Museum, inv. 111475
From the back wall of a *cubiculum* in the House of Jason (IX, 5, 18)

Third Style central panel portraying Europa, daughter of the king of Phoenicia, who, while playing on the seashore with her handmaidens, was approached by Zeus in the form of a white bull, which lured her into seating herself on its back and thereupon carried her off, across the sea to Crete. There, after bearing Zeus three sons, she married the King of Crete, who adopted her sons, one of whom, Minos, became his heir. Europa is shown seated on the bull in a rocky landscape painted in tones of gray on a white ground, against which the figures, which were painted first, stand out in sharp relief. The landscape, with its central oak tree (the tree sacred to Zeus), echoes the central scene.

On the left-hand wall of the same bedroom *(cubiculum)*, by the same hand, was the painting of Pan and the nymphs (No. 114) and on the right-hand wall a painting of Hercules, Deianira, and the centaur Nessus. Common to all three paintings was the symbolic use of trees within the landscape.
Schefold, *WP* 263-264; Peters 96f.

129

130
Wall painting: Nile landscape
Width 1.41 m, height 38 cm
Naples Museum, inv. 8561
From Herculaneum, 1748

A typical combination of Nilotic flora and fauna with elements of Egyptianizing architecture, from the dado (lower zone) of a Third Style wall. Within a setting of marsh and river, with date palms and lotus flowers are, on the left, a crocodile; in the center, an island enclosure with buildings made of reeds, including a tower similar to that shown in No. 190; on the right, an Egyptian goose and a hippopotamus on a rocky island.
Pitture di Ercolano I, 50, 263.

130

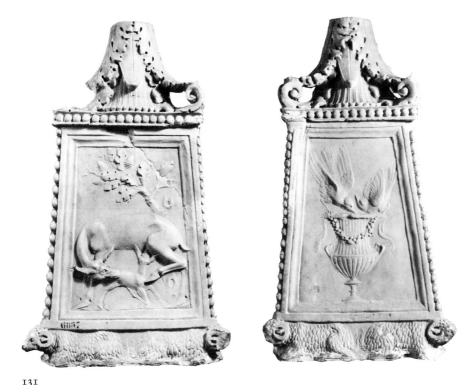

131

131
Three-sided base for a candelabrum
Pentelic marble
Height 56 cm
Naples Museum, inv. 6857
From one of the sites in the Vesuvius area

The base, which is carried on the backs of three crouching rams, is topped with an inverted capital, in the center of which is the socket for a bronze candelabrum. The three faces are carved in low relief; on one side two rams reach up to nibble grapes on the top of a candelabrum with a similarly three-sided base; on the second side two birds (ravens?) drinking from a fluted vase (*crater*) hung with garlands; and on the third a doe suckling a fawn in the shade of an oak tree. Large numbers of such ornate pieces of marble furniture were being produced in the later first century B.C. and the first century A.D. by Athenian workshops operating within the academic traditions of late Hellenistic decorative sculpture. There is a piece probably from the same workshop in the Museo Nazionale Romano (inv. 371; *Annali dell'Inst.* XXII [1850] 60ff.).

132
Bronze candelabrum (lamp stand) and three hanging bronze lamps
Height 56.7 cm
Naples Museum, inv. 72226
From Pompeii

The shaft of this candelabrum takes the form of a growing, twisted vine with leaves and tendrils; the largest of the tendrils become the supports for the hanging lamps, two of which are in the form of snail shells. Palmettes and tendrils inlaid in silver decorate the top of the flat base. A pair of bulls' skulls draped with ribbons, a *thyrsus*, and laurel wreaths are inlaid with silver on the front of the round drum from which the shaft springs. Since a splendid example of this type of vegetable-form lamp stand was found at Pergamum, it is very likely the Romans inherited a taste for such works of decorative art from the cities of western Asia Minor.

Chiurazzi 227, no. 494; Spinazzola pl. 292.

132

133
Relief with scenes from the myth of Telephos
Pentelic marble
Length 1.20 m, height 52 cm
Naples Museum, inv. 76/128
From Herculaneum, House of the Telephos Relief

Originally set into the wall plaster of a small anteroom to a *triclinium*, the relief shows two episodes in the history of the Trojan Wars. Achilles, on his way to Troy, had landed by mistake on the territory of Telephos, king of Mysia, who received from Achilles' spear a wound in the thigh that refused to heal. Achilles consulted an oracle, which told him he

133

would only reach Troy if Telephos would consent to guide him. Telephos too consulted an oracle and was told that only "he that wounded could cure." In the left-hand scene Achilles is consulting the oracle. In the right-hand scene he is scraping rust from his spearhead ("he that wounded") onto Telephos' wound, effecting a rapid cure.

The relief belongs to a large series showing mythological scenes, produced by Athenian workshops in the later first century B.C. for Roman patrons, who had them set into decorative painted or marble-veneered wall schemes in both public and private buildings. Wall paintings of the Second Style (e.g., the House of the Lararium, I, 6, 4, *cubiculum*) sometimes incorporated painted imitations.

There are indications that the relief was originally brightly colored.

MdI v (1952) 147; C. Bauchhenss-Thüriedl, *Der Mythos von Telephos in der antiken Bildkunst* (Würzburg 1971) 91; Maiuri, *Ercolano* 355.

134
Wall painting: satyr and maenad
Width 37 cm, height 37 cm
Naples Museum, inv. 9135
From the *tablinum* of the House of the Dioscuri

This painting, like so many found in the early days of Pompeian excavation, had been chopped out of a larger wall composition. The dancing couple would have been the center of a panel of a Fourth Style wall, sailing on its empty light blue expanse as though through the upper air. A muscular, sunburned young satyr,

crowned with leaves and carrying a cloth weighted down with the land's produce, embraces a white-skinned maenad. She brandishes the *thyrsus,* symbol of sacred revelry; the wind of their flight blows the drapery back from her nude torso. Flickering highlights add to the feeling of motion; black, decisive shadows lend weight to the strong little bodies.

Spinazzola pl. 145; Schefold, *WP* 117.

135 (color plate, vol. I, p. 26)
Fragment of Fourth Style wall painting
Width 98 cm, height 90 cm
Naples Museum, inv. 8514
From Pompeii

Fragment from the upper zone of an early Fourth Style wall, including the upper border and an *aedicula* set in a formal quasi-architectural scheme of delicate garlands and slender rods entwined with tendrils, reminiscent of fine late Third Style work (as in the White Triclinium in the House of M. Lucretius, IX, 3, 5). Within the *aedicula* is the figure of a woman with flowing draperies, poised as if flying.

134

135

137

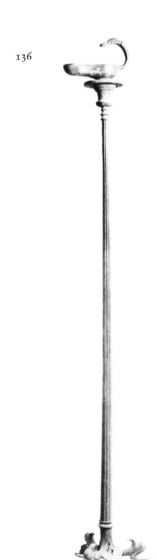

136

136a
Bronze candelabrum (lamp stand)
Height 1.12 m
Naples Museum, inv. 78537

The tall, gently tapering, fluted stem springs from a three-legged base and carries a lamp stand in the form of a vase (*crater*). Each leg consists of the hind leg of a lion, resting on a low drum and springing from beneath an upward-curling leaf. Ivy leaves fill the angles between the legs. Early first century A.D.
Pernice IV, 47f., fig. 60.

136b
Bronze lamp
Height 11 cm, length 20 cm
Naples Museum, inv. 72483
From Pompeii

The reservoir and nozzle of this lamp are drawn out into an elongated tear-drop shape, which is emphasized by a gentle molding similar to that on No. 161. The handle is arched over the filling hole and is decorated with a dolphin's head holding a cockle shell in its mouth. This motif is also found on the feet of bronze candelabra.

137
Wall painting: Pyramus and Thisbe
Height 1.05 m, width 80 cm
Naples Museum, inv. 111483
From the *triclinium* on the left of the northern *ala* of House IX, 5, 14

This artless painting, the central panel of a Fourth Style wall, represents the final scene of the story of the unhappy Babylonian lovers, Pyramus and Thisbe, "the most lamentable comedy, and most cruel death of Pyramus and Thisby," which Bottom the Weaver and his company presented at the court of King Theseus in Shakespeare's *Midsummer Night's Dream*. Pyramus, believing Thisbe dead, has killed himself beneath a mulberry tree; she, finding him dead, is stabbing herself with his sword. The pillar supporting an urn represents the tomb where they were to have met. There is a Third Style version of the same composition in the garden *triclinium* of the House of "Loreius Tiburtinus" (II, 2, 2-5) and another in a Fourth Style *triclinium* in the House of M. Lucretius Fronto (IV, II, I).
Schefold, WP 260.

139   140   141

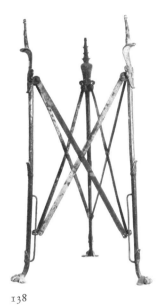

138

138
Bronze folding tripod
Height 58.2 cm
Naples Museum, old inv. 1452
From Pompeii

The uprights of this tripod consist of three rods, which rest on animal's-paw feet; they are punctuated by three sheath leaves, and at the top each terminates in a decorative finial in the form of an *uraeus*, crowned with a lotus bud and springing from two small birds' heads. Hinged to the inner face just below the finial are two transverse struts, each of

which is pivoted at the center to one of its neighbors and linked to another at the bottom by means of a ring that is free to slide up and down the length of a rectangular loop on the inner face of the upright. Although the mechanism closely resembles that of adjustable stands that could accommodate bowls of various sizes, in this case there were only two possible positions: closed, with the uprights and transverse rods all folded together, or open, with some circular object, probably a flanged bowl, resting on the top of the finials and locking the legs in a fully splayed position.
Ceci pl. IV, no. 4; *MB* 5 (Naples 1829) pl. LX.

139
Wall painting: basket
Height 24 cm, width 20 cm
Naples Museum, inv. 8689
From one of the sites in the Vesuvius area

The basket, on a white ground, occupied the center of one of the lateral panels of a Third Style wall. The most plausible identification is that it represents a work basket containing spindles of colored wool, one of which is shown resting against the rim of the basket.
Beyen, *Stilleben* 23f.; Croisille 44.

140
Wall painting: head of Pan
Height 19 cm, width 11 cm
Naples Museum, inv. 9126
From Herculaneum

The head has been cut from an ornamental frieze in a Fourth Style wall.

141 (color plate, vol. I, p. 68)
Wall painting: medallion with busts of Dionysus and a maenad
Diameter 44.5 cm
Naples Museum, inv. 9284
From Herculaneum

Dionysus, god of wine and of ecstatic liberation, is shown with a wreath of grapes and vine leaves; in his right hand he holds a drinking cup (*cantharus*) and in his left, resting against his shoulder, the characteristic Dionysiac staff, or *thyrsus*. Behind him, her hand on his shoulder, is one of his attendant devotees, a maenad; she wears a mantle and earrings, with flowers in her hair.

Medallions such as this, containing real or mythological portraits, were placed in the middle of the lateral panels of many Fourth Style compositions (e.g., in the *tablinum* of the House of the Bicentenary at Herculaneum). This one, from its subject matter, may have adorned a *triclinium;* its companion piece (inv. 9283) showed Dionysus and a satyr.
Elia no. 304.

142

143

142
Bronze stool
Height 27 cm, length 29.4 cm, width
(side with curve) 26 cm
Pompeii, Storerooms, inv. 13355

Metal was widely used in fine Roman
furniture; large pieces were ornamented
or sheathed with bronze, while a small
accessory like this could be made entirely
of metal. The material makes possible
airy, attenuated supports and fine openwork ornament. The struts between the
legs are made up of tendrils, which
enframe blossoms in the finely detailed
panels under the seat. The simple panels
on the long sides have been almost entirely
restored. The concave upper surface
shows that this piece was a stool, not a
table, and probably held a cushion. There
are similar seats in Naples, London, and
Berlin.
Cf. G. M. A. Richter, *The Furniture of the
Greeks, Etruscans and Romans* (London
1966) 111, fig. 564.

143 (color plate, vol. I, p. 70)
Wall painting: Pan and Hermaphroditus
Width 1.25 m, height 74 cm
Naples Museum, inv. 27700
From the atrium of the House of the
Dioscuri (VI, 9, 6)

Part of the upper zone of a Fourth Style
scheme, from above the doorway leading
from the *fauces* into the atrium. Hermaphroditus, one of the most curious
by-products of Greek mythology, was a
minor divinity of bisexual form, with
female breasts and male genitals. In this
picture he is seated by a pool, and Pan,
aroused by his apparently female charms,
has just discovered his mistake. Beyond
Pan is a tower within a square enclosure,
set in a rocky landscape. On the right is a
statue of Priapus, standing on a pedestal
and holding a cornucopia.
Richardson pl. 23.1; Schefold, *WP* 116;
Peters 138; Kraus and von Matt no. 276.

144, 145 (color plate, vol. I, p. 22)
**Wall paintings: fantasy architecture from
a Fourth Style wall**
Height 1.88 m, width 52 cm
Naples Museum, inv. 9710, 9707
From Pompeii, May 1760

Narrow vertical panels depicting slender
fantasy architecture in receding perspective are commonly used to frame the
central panel in one type of Fourth Style
wall. On the broad plane surface of the
central panel in the scheme from which
these elements came was painted a small
framed picture of Perseus and Andromeda
(Naples Museum, inv. 8995), and in the
middle of each lateral panel were roundels
(see also Nos. 2, 141). One of these was
the famous "Sappho" (Naples Museum,
inv. 9084).
A. Allroggen-Bedel, "Herkunft und
ursprünglicher Dekorationszusammen-
hang einiger in Essen ausgestellter
Fragmente von Wandmalereien," *Neue
Forschungen in Pompeji* 118f., fig. 95b.

146 (color plate, vol. I, p. 25)
**Wall painting: Theseus, slayer of the
Minotaur**
Width 88 cm, height 97 cm
Naples Museum, inv. 9043
From the *exedra* off the peristyle in the
House of Gavius Rufus (VII, 2, 16)

The central panel of the left-hand wall of
a Fourth Style scheme. It shows Theseus
victorious from his battle with the Minotaur, the bull-headed monster of Crete to
whom the Athenians had each year to
send a tribute of youths and maidens. The
Minotaur lies dead in the entrance to his
lair, the Labyrinth, and his destined victims press round Theseus in gratitude. A
finer version of the same Greek original
(Naples Museum, inv. 9049) was found in
the Basilica at Herculaneum. The companion pieces of the picture at Pompeii
were (on the opposite wall, inv. 9044)
Pirithous, the companion of Theseus, re-
ceiving the centaurs and (on the rear wall,
inv. 9449) Dionysus, Aphrodite, and the
sun god, Helios.
Schefold, *WP* 136; Bianchi Bandinelli 110f.,
illustrating both this piece (fig. 116) and the
piece from Herculaneum (fig. 115).

147
Panel from a painted ceiling
Width 88 cm, height 82 cm
Naples Museum, inv. 9973
From Pompeii

The design, here reduced to a formal
pattern, is reminiscent of a ceiling coffer.
A small head of Medusa occupies the
center.

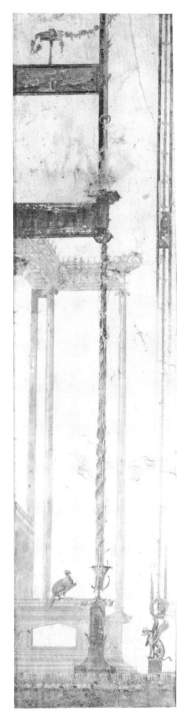

144

146

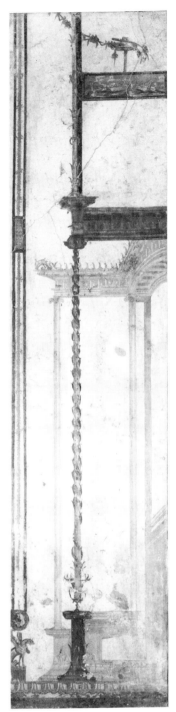

145

147

148

149

150

148, 149
Wall painting: pair of sea centaurs
Height 34 cm, width 24 cm
Height 30 cm, width 18 cm
Naples Museum, inv. 8888, 8887
From one of the sites in the Vesuvius area

Acroteria from a pair of panels of Fourth Style fantasy architecture similar to those flanking the panel of the Infant Hercules in the House of the Vettii (see page 100). They are shown blowing horns and holding tambourines.

150 (color plate, vol. I, p. 24)
Wall painting: woman giving water to a traveler
Width 44 cm, height 38 cm
Naples Museum, inv. 9106
From the *tablinum* of the House of the Dioscuri (VI, 9, 6)

The picture formed part of a longer landscape frieze, with painted moldings top and bottom, over the side panels of a Fourth Style wall (as in the atrium of the House of the Menander). In front of a rustic shelter made of canes, a woman, seated on a circular platform and wearing a conical hat, dips a beaker from a jar and hands it to a traveler, whose dog sits waiting for him.

Spinazzola-Aurigemma 580; Richardson 124f.; Schefold, *WP* 118; Peters 164.

151
Portable pottery brazier
Height 17 cm, width 32 cm, depth 24 cm
Naples Museum, inv. 76/198
From one of the sites in the Vesuvius area

The brazier is a simple box, with a series of holes pierced through the top to allow the heat to escape and provided with two lug handles for carrying.

152 (color plate, vol. I, p. 69)
Wall painting: Phaedra and Hippolytus
Width 1.03 m, height 1.04 m
Naples Museum, inv. 9041
From Herculaneum

Phaedra, wife of Theseus, King of Athens, had conceived a guilty passion for her stepson, Hippolytus, a passion that he rejected; whereupon Phaedra accused him of trying to seduce her. He was subsequently killed while out hunting, and she hanged herself. In this painting Phaedra's old nurse tells Hippolytus of her mistress' love, as he is setting out for the hunt. The scene, of which there were several variant copies at Pompeii, is based on a Hellenistic original, which in turn was inspired by Euripides' tragedy *Hippolytus*. In this version, from a Fourth Style wall, Phaedra has been given a Flavian court hairstyle; it must have been painted very shortly before A.D. 79.

Schefold, *WP* 335.

153 (color plate, vol. I, p. 15)
Wall painting: the Three Graces
Width 53 cm, height 56 cm
Naples Museum, inv. 9236
From the *tablinum* of the House of Titus Dentatus Panthera (IX, 2, 16)

Panel cut from the middle of a Fourth Style wall. The Three Graces, or *Charites*, daughters of Zeus by various mothers, personified beauty, grace, and intellectual and moral wisdom. There are innumerable examples of this group both in painting and in sculpture, all obviously copied from the same original, presumably a well-known Hellenistic sculpture. The Graces are commonly portrayed, as here, holding or wreathed with spring flowers. This explains the presence of flowers in the landscape setting, a feature not represented elsewhere in Pompeian mythological scenes.

Schefold, *WP* 242; Peters 139.

154
Bronze apparatus for heating liquids
Height 51 cm, base 43 cm square
Naples Museum, inv. 72986
From a villa near Stabiae

Rather like a samovar, this apparatus was designed to maintain a continuous supply of hot wine or any other hot fluid. The liquid was poured into a gently tapering, churn-shaped container (A) with a hinged lid; from this it was free to pass through a tall, narrow duct (B) into the hollow walls of a cylindrical fire-box (C), from which it could be drawn off as required through a tap (D) in the shape of a lion's head. The source of heat was a charcoal fire in the middle of the fire-box. Fuel could be stored in the square, four-legged tray, which also served to contain the ashes. As long as the level of the liquid within the main container was kept above that of the tap, a constant supply was assured, piping hot. In addition to the tap there are a number of applied bronze fittings: on the main container a comic actor's mask (see No. 167) and a handle in the form of a miniature bust of Mercury; on the rim of the fire-box three swans poised for flight; and on the tray four legs in the form of sirens, and four drop handles.

MB 4 (Rome 1841) pl. xx.

152

153

151

154

173

156

155

155a
Bronze candelabrum (lamp stand)
Height 1.265 m
Naples Museum, inv. 78485
From one of the sites in the Vesuvius area

The slender shaft is made in the form of a bamboo cane, which divides into three at the top to carry the round plate on which the lamp stood. The three feet arch outward from the base of the stem, with long, tongue-shaped leaves between them. Such candelabra appear commonly in Pompeian wall paintings of the Second and Third Style.

155b
Bronze oil lamp
Height 13 cm, length 20 cm
Naples Museum, inv. 72490
From Pompeii

The two stems of the handle support a vertical escutcheon in the shape of an

openwork heart. The nozzle is plain except for the rosettes at the point of junction. The filling hole is fitted with a small plug, which is attached to the base of the handle by means of a chain of twisted loops of bronze wire.

156 (color plate, vol. I, p. 66)
Dionysiac scene in marble intarsia
Slate and colored marbles
Length 67 cm, height 23 cm
Naples Museum, inv. 9977
From the House of the Colored Capitals (VII, 4, 31-51)

One of a pair of Dionysiac scenes found in the *tablinum,* where they were probably used on the walls as panel pictures *(pinakes).* On the left a maenad dances in ecstasy, with torch and *tympanon;* on the right a satyr clutches a *thyrsus* and is waving a goatskin; and in the center is a small shrine. The companion piece portrays a maenad dancing toward a Priapus herm; a statue on a pedestal; a nude youth with a panther; and a tree beside a sacred pillar monument or baetyl (as in the sacro-idyllic landscapes).

The technique is that of intarsia, a sophisticated variant of *opus sectile,* composed of shaped and inscribed pieces of colored marble (*giallo antico* from Africa, *fior di persico* from Euboea, and *paesina verde* and *palombino* from Italy) cut out and fitted into a slate panel. Third quarter of the first century A.D.
Mau, *Bull Inst* XLVI (1874), 98; Elia, *BdA* IX (1929) 265ff.; Dohrn, *RM* 72 (1965) 131; Kraus and von Matt no. 272.

157
Crescent-shaped terracotta lamp with three nozzles
Height 4 cm (with reflector, 9 cm) length 14 cm, width 13 cm
Pompeii, Storerooms, inv. 14040
Found in the house of Fabius Rufus (Insula occidentalis)

Fashioned of lustrous red-brown clay, this richly decorated lamp is of an unusual shape and is also exceptional in having three heart-shaped nozzles rather than the usual one or two. The characteristic form of the nozzle indicates a date in the third quarter of the first century A.D. Both the date and the relative rarity of this type of

lamp at Pompeii suggest that it may have been a new fashion in lamps whose production was cut short by the eruption.

An eagle, symbol of Jupiter, perches on the outer curve of the crescent to act as a reflector. In low relief on the well of the lamp, a thin crescent moon curves around the filling hole, with a star on either side to carry out the celestial motif.

Roman lamps burned low-grade olive oil with a fiber wick. The two small holes at each point of the inner crescent allowed air to circulate within the body of the lamp for better burning.
Andreae, *Pompeji* 96, no. 58.

157

158

159

160

161

158
Terracotta lamp
Height 10 cm, length 17 cm
Pompeii, Antiquarium, inv. 12836

This lamp solves the problem of a multiple light source in a novel way. Instead of simply increasing the number of nozzles, as in Nos. 159-162, the potter has joined together a number of independent lamps of standard forms: a large round-nozzled lamp as base for two small "factory lamps," a type introduced in the last years of Pompeii. The hemispherical cup with serrated edge mounted on the large lamp's handle may have been intended for incense. The cup is surrounded with four fighting cocks with victory palms. Stamped circles decorate the background. An oak wreath fills the central disc of the large lamp. The lamp represents an attempt by an artisan trained in mass-production techniques to create a sculpturally interesting as well as functionally specialized object.

159
Glazed terracotta lamp with two nozzles
Height 22 cm, length 37.8 cm
Naples Museum, inv. 76/165
From Pompeii

The vine leaf is a simplified version of that found on bronze lamps (No. 160). The nozzles are joined to the body by large volutes, of which the outer pair end in

horses' heads. The well in the middle is decorated with an ovolo border and scalloped fluting radiating from the filling hole.

The blue-green glaze, colored with copper oxide, is characteristic of a substantial group of fine terracotta objects, including small statuettes and fountain figures, as well as lamps and pottery vessels. There were several centers of production employing this technique, but it has been suggested that these large lamps with horse's-head volutes were imported from Cnidos in southwestern Asia Minor, where large numbers of them have been found, and that the glaze was applied by a local potter.

160
Two-nozzled oil lamp on a low stand
Bronze
Lamp: height 26.5 cm, length 40.5 cm
Stand: height 10.3 cm, diameter 11.5 cm
Naples Museum, inv. 72284 and 72270
From Pompeii

In both the shape of the body and the vine-leaf handle, the lamp resembles the example copied in glazed terracotta, No. 159, except that the volutes linking the nozzles to the body are plain. The vine leaf is also found used decoratively between the legs of lamp stands (e.g., Naples Museum, inv. 72251; Pernice IV, fig. 78).

The stand is of a common three-legged type, enriched with oak leaves springing between three lion's-paw feet. Such lamps stood on side tables, and they are also found on the counters of shops and bars.
Pernice IV, fig. 81; Chiurazzi no. 523.

161
Two-nozzled oil lamp on a low stand
Bronze
Lamp: height 20.3 cm, length 28 cm
Stand: height 15.6 cm, diameter 13 cm
Naples Museum, inv. 72331 and 72212
From Pompeii

The lamp is cast in bronze, its ring foot and the ornate handle added as separate castings. The handle consists of a bat-like creature, with a panther's head and spread wings, perched on the volutes of an acanthus palmette. The small circular stand consists of a molded top and, below it, twelve equally spaced, arched projections, three of which are prolonged downward and end in lion's paws. First century A.D.
Pernice IV, 58, fig. 79 (the stand).

175

162 (color plate, vol. I, p. 31)
Gold lamp with two nozzles
Height 15.1 cm, length 23.2 cm
Naples Museum, inv. 25000
From Pompeii

The body bears a design of lotus leaves similar to that found on late Hellenistic bowls in precious metals or their pottery equivalents; it was worked in relief from the outside with a punch, after filling the interior with pitch. The leaf-shaped reflector in front of the handle is similarly worked with a palmette design. The plain spouts and base were cast separately and soldered into place. The lid, now missing, would normally have been the most highly decorated part.

The discovery of this lamp was one of the sensations of the excavations of 1863.
Breglia no. 1025; Siviero no. 341; *Bull Inst* XXXV (1863) 90-91.

162

163

163
Bronze lantern
Height of lantern 19 cm, total height (excluding modern brass hook) 39 cm
Naples Museum, inv. 72078
From Pompeii

The wick holder, with a cap that could be removed for cleaning and refilling, is set in the middle of a circular base plate, which stands on three small feet. The flame was originally protected by semi-transparent sheets of horn slotted between the double ring of bronze mounted on the base plate and a similar ring above, which is soldered onto the backs of two vertical rods in the form of pilasters with Doric capitals. To the tops of the latter were attached the rings and chains, linked to the ends of a yoke-shaped cross bar, by which the lantern was held. The lid, a shallow inverted bowl, is pierced with a pattern of holes for ventilation when closed. The lantern could also be carried with the lid raised. A chain attached to the top, ends in a short rod slotted through the main carrying bar, with a ring to stop it slipping too far, and has its own yoke handle. Rings on either side of the lid loop around the main chains to keep the lid centered over the lantern body.
Cf. *BMC Lamps* no. 1495.

164
Bronze plaque with a lion's-head ring handle
Width 19.5 cm, height 12.8 cm
Naples Museum, inv. 72738
From Pompeii

One of a pair. The four holes show that it was attached to some large wooden object, probably a door. Although appearing also on other large objects such as chests or vats, handles of this form are very common in representations of doors in classical art.

164

165

165
Bronze drop handle
Mounting plate: width 19 cm, height 3.3 cm
Handle: width 17.5 cm, drop 7.7 cm
Naples Museum, inv. 72980
From Pompeii

The ends of the handle are in the form of elongated animal's heads, perhaps intended to portray hounds with their ears pressed flat against their necks. The absence of nail-holes shows that this piece was probably soldered onto some portable bronze object, such as a brazier or a heating apparatus (see No. 154).

166
Bronze door handle
Length 31.3 cm, width 4.8 cm
Naples Museum, inv. 70277
From the Vesuvius area, possibly from the Villa of Publius Fannius Synistor at Boscoreale

The handle was mounted as shown in the diagram, with the grip fixed through the thin bronze base plate, and through slots in the thicker door plate, to two levers on springs that it could raise or drop by slid-

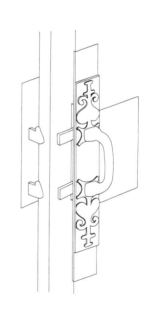

166

167 168 169 171

ing up or down. On the face of the base plate, developing from cusped rectangles below the feet of the grip, are heart-shaped motifs turning into volutes and ending in motifs like the hilt of a sword with a strongly marked rib down the central axis. This combination of motifs is found in Campanian bronzeware as early as the second century B.C. It was used on door handles certainly by the early first century B.C. and enjoyed a long popularity.

Cf. Pernice IV, 63; *JdAI* XIX (1904) 15f.

167
Bronze ornament in the form of a theater mask
Height 5.3 cm
Naples Museum, inv. "94"
From one of the sites in the Vesuvius area

The mask, cast solid, represents a slave in New Comedy. It was probably applied to an elaborate piece of domestic bronze equipment such as the heating apparatus, No. 154.

168
Miniature herm in bronze
Height 19.5 cm
Naples Museum, inv. 5343
Found in Herculaneum, October 1764

The herm, in the form of a child, is hollow, with an iron rod running down the back of it. It was evidently the foot of some large piece of iron furniture.

Bronzi di Ercolano 2, 356f., pl. LXXXIX; cf. K. A. Neugebauer, *Die griechischen Bronzen der klassischen Zeit und des Hellenismus* (Berlin 1951) 27, no. 18.

170

169
Bronze bust of a satyr in high relief
Height 16 cm
Naples Museum, unnumbered
Probably from Herculaneum or Pompeii

This wild companion of Bacchus has a snake twisted around his shoulders. Horns sprout through his bushy hair, and tufts of hair swirl on his chest and forehead.

Busts or plaques of this type were fashioned to be applied to the heavy chests in which the householders of Pompeii kept their valuables. The dramatic turn of the figure's head, shoulders, and arm indicates the prototype was created in western Asia Minor, probably near Pergamum, after about 200 B.C.

Chiurazzi 251, no. 574; Ruesch 367, no. 1608.

170
Bronze ring with a Medusa head
Diameter 11.2 cm
Naples Museum, inv. 72969
From Pompeii

This handle, from the door of a cupboard or a wooden coffer, consists of a grooved ring hinged at the top to a circular base plate, upon which is portrayed in relief the

head of Medusa, the snake-haired female monster whose glance turned all who looked upon her to stone and who was slain by Perseus (see No. 307). By an easy extension of ideas a Medusa head was thought to protect the object it adorned. Its shape is well suited to filling circular spaces, and it is used commonly in handles of this sort. The eyes are inlaid with silver, in the center of which is a hole for the pupil, which may have been made of colored glass.

Pernice IV, 19.

171
Ivory panel from a piece of wooden furniture
Height 10.5 cm, width 6 cm
Naples Museum, inv. 10158
From one of the sites in the Vesuvius area

The panel probably formed part of the veneer on an elaborately turned leg of a wooden couch or stool. Its dimensions and slightly tapering convex shape are closely paralleled by ivory plaques in the Field Museum of Natural History, Chicago, thought to have come from a funerary couch.

Carved in relief is the figure of the Muse Terpsichore, patron of the dance, holding a plectrum in her right hand and a lyre beside her left shoulder.

Cf. C. L. Ransom, *Studies in Ancient Furniture*, 1 (Chicago 1905) 56f. and 102f.

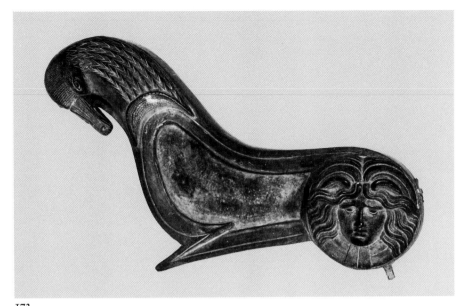

172

174, 175
Decorative intarsia strips, from a banqueting couch
Length 56 cm, height 3.9 cm
Length 56.7 cm, height 4.4 cm
Naples Museum, old inv. 5451, 70995
From Pompeii

Two almost identical panels of bronze, delicately ornamented with inlaid silverwork in the long, narrow recessed panel and in the shorter, flat panels at the two ends. Comparison with another, longer piece in the Naples Museum (inv. 70992) shows that the designs on the end panels, meaningless as they stand, are abbreviated versions of a scheme with acanthus leaves and sprays of tiny leaves set symmetrically about a central palmette. The craftsman was using repertory motifs fitted as best they might be within the space available.

Panels of this sort were used to decorate and strengthen the long horizontal members of couches, also sometimes on footstools. They were recessed into the wood with the flange uppermost.
Mau-Kelsey 361f., fig. 180.

172
Bronze couch ornament (fulcrum)
Length 44 cm
Naples Museum, inv. 78/98
From the Vesuvius area

The type of couch from which this bronze ornament comes was, like most at Pompeii, an invention of Hellenistic times, reproduced with only subtle variations of detail and proportion. It stood on high turned legs; a frame with stretched webbing carried the mattress. There was a low headboard, contoured to support cushions on which a diner could lean. The ornament here was a bracket decorating and reinforcing the edge of the headboard. It combines a graceful duck's head, a favorite motif of Greek metalwork and furniture, with sinuous moldings and a face of Medusa. The organic, irregular form of the support has been broken down into representational components. The workmanship of this example is particularly bold, stiff, and definite, far from the sketchy vitality of Hellenistic examples. Details like the duck's feathers are engraved after casting.
Cf. G. M. A. Richter, *The Furniture of the Greeks, Etruscans and Romans* (London 1966) figs. 532, 533.

173

173
Small bronze bust of a goddess of plenty
Height 10 cm
Naples Museum, inv. 5150
Found in Herculaneum

Cast bronze fitting, probably from the lower end of the curved support (*fulcrum*) on a couch. The figure wears a short veil over the head, covering a high hair-piece, and round her neck is a silver necklace of beads from which hang large, lozenge-shaped silver pendants. Her eyes too are inlaid with silver. In the folds of her loose tunic she carries a selection of fruit, identifying her as Pomona, the Italian goddess of orchards and gardens, or possibly as Fortuna, goddess of plenty.
Bronzi di Ercolano, I, 47, pl. x; *MB* 9 (Rome 1845) 352, pl. XXXVII.

176
Decorative intarsia strip, from a piece of furniture
Silver on bronze
Length 61.7 cm, height 3.8 cm
Naples Museum, inv. 70990
From Pompeii

Despite the obvious resemblance of this piece to Nos. 174 and 175, the absence of any flange along the upper edge suggests that it was let into some other piece of wooden furniture, such as a table. The vine scroll of the two long recessed panels would have been appropriate to a table or stool used in a dining room. The central panel contains an elaborate formal rosette, the two end panels a section of a latticework design with simpler, eight-petaled rosettes.

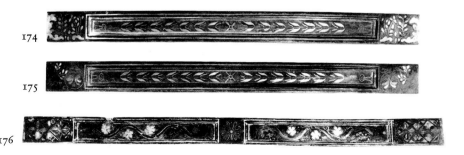

174

175

176

V Cults and Beliefs

Hall of the Mysteries, Pompeii

177
Wall painting: the arrival of Io at Canopus
Height 80 cm, width 66 cm
Naples Museum, inv. 9555
From the room north of the atrium in the
House of the Duke of Aumale (VI, 9, 1)

From the center panel of a late Third Style
scheme, the painting illustrates a scene
from the story of Io, the virgin priestess of
Hera at Argos, who had the misfortune to
attract the amorous eye of Zeus. Trans-
formed by Hera into a white heifer, she
was watched over by the hundred-eyed
herdsman Argus, until the latter was slain
and Io released by Hermes. After inter-
minable wanderings she found haven in
Egypt, where she was kindly received by
Isis and resumed human form, giving birth
to Epaphos, legendary ancestor of, among
others, the royal house of Argos. Within
the Isiac cult she tended to be assimilated
with the cow goddess Hathor.

In this painting Io is borne by the river
god of the Nile into the presence of Isis,
who is shown enthroned in her great
sanctuary at Canopus, near Alexandria.
Isis holds the royal cobra of Egypt in her
left hand; her feet rest on a crocodile, and,
facing her, a small sphinx symbolizes the
land of Egypt. Behind her are two white-
robed attendants who hold *sistra* (see
Nos. 186, 187) and the messenger's staff
(*caduceus*) of Hermes; and at her side,
finger to his lips, stands the child god
Harpocrates (see Nos. 182, 183). Io's past
wanderings are symbolized by the pair of
horns on her forehead. Another painting
of this scene, larger and of superior quality, clearly derived from the same Hellenistic original, was found in the Temple of
Isis (Elia, *Mon Pitt* 27-30).
Curtius fig. 129.

177

179

178

178
Section of a painted frieze
Length 2.18 m, height 82 cm
Naples Museum, inv. 8546
From the portico wall of the Temple
of Isis

The frieze, on a black ground, represents
an ornate acanthus plant scroll, in the
spirals of which are lotus-flower heads alternating with pygmies and with animals
and birds associated with Isis: from left to
right, a pygmy running, a cobra, a hippopotamus, and an eagle. Below the frieze is
part of the central zone of the wall, including the top of the frame of one of the
panels, which contained a landscape
similar to No. 190. In the frame is a small
panel containing a theater mask.

179
Wall painting: seated figure of Bes
Width 66 cm, height 1.14 m
Naples Museum, inv. 8916
From the Temple of Isis, from the west
wall of the smaller of the two rooms at
the west end of the sanctuary (see also
No. 180)

179

This inner room, possibly used for initia-
tions, was decorated on the west, north,
and east walls with figures relating to the
cult of Isis, all very broadly executed on a
white ground with little or no attempt at
relative scale.

The Egyptian god of the dance, char-
acteristically portrayed as a squat, obese
figure, is seated nude on a throne, with his
hands on his knees and a large flower on
his head.
Tran tam Tinh, *Pompéi* 145, no. 52; Elia,
Mon Pitt III. 4, 21.

180
Wall painting of an ibis
Width 56 cm, height 82 cm
Naples Museum, inv. 8562
From the Temple of Isis, from the north
wall of the same room as No. 179

This large Egyptian ibis occupied the
center of the north wall between representations of the discovery of Osiris and a
lion. On the west wall Isis, Serapis, and
Bes (No. 179) sat enthroned, and facing
them were the bull Apis and a number of
other sacred animals: monkey, sheep,
mole, jackal, sparrowhawk, vulture,
cobra, and mongoose (ichneumon). The
ibis has a lotus flower on the top of its
head and a stalk of wheat in its beak.
Tran tam Tinh, *Pompéi* 144, no. 48; Elia,
Mon Pitt III. 4, 22.

181
Bronze statuette of Isis-Fortuna
Height 33.5 cm (43 cm with base)
Naples Museum, inv. 5313
From Herculaneum

The richly draped and adorned goddess
wears an Egyptian headdress with the
solar disc and the horns of Hathor. She
holds a rudder and a horn of plenty out
of which emerge fruits and a pyramidal
object usually interpreted as a kind of
sacrificial cake. These attributes form an
allegory of navigation through the seas of
life to the land of plenty and also symbolize the link between the grain of Egypt
and the ports of Italy. An ivy garland, a
bull's skull, and two eight-pointed stars
are inlaid in silver on the base.
Chiurazzi 81, no. 131.

180

181

182
Bronze statuette of Harpocrates
Height 8 cm
Naples Museum, inv. 5329
From the *lararium* in the House of the
emperor Joseph II (VIII, 2, 38-39)

Harpocrates, in origin the Egyptian child-
god Harpa-Khruti, son of Isis and Serapis,
is shown in the conventional attitude of
childhood, with his finger on his lips, later
misinterpreted by the Romans as a gesture
of silence. His curly hair is crowned with
ivy leaves and a top-knot. A *bulla* (see
No. 40) hangs round his neck. On his back
he has little wings, a quiver, and a ring for
suspension. He rests his left arm, holding
a cornucopia (horn of plenty) entwined by
a snake, on a knobbly tree trunk.
PAH 1, i, 233; *MB* 12 (Naples 1850) pl. xxx. 2;
RM 2 (1887) 119; Boyce no. 349 note; Tran
tam Tinh, *Pompéi* 162, no. 107.

183
Bronze statuette of Harpocrates
Height 8.3 cm (12.2 cm with base)
Naples Museum, inv. 5368
From one of the sites in the Vesuvius area

Similar to No. 182, but the snake is coiled
round his left thigh, and he holds the
cornucopia unsupported. Probably from a
lararium.
Tran tam Tinh, *Pompéi* 164, no. 111.

184
Terracotta figurine of a priest
Height 18 cm
Naples Museum, inv. 20477
From Pompeii(?)

The figure, dressed in long robes edged
with a richly embroidered border, holds
some object, perhaps a key, in his left hand
and is thought to represent a priest. Which
particular cult he served is uncertain.
Levi no. 865.

185
Two figures of ibises
Marble and bronze
Length 39 cm, height 25 cm
Length 41 cm, height 25.5 cm

182   183   184

Naples Museum, Egyptian Collection,
inv. 765 and 766
Possibly from the Temple of Isis

The heads, necks, and legs of the birds are
in bronze, while the bodies are made of
white marble, following their natural
coloring. The technique of combining
such materials at this date is most unusual.
Tran tam Tinh, *Pompéi* 175, nos. 145 and
146; *Pitture di Ercolano* 5, 119.

186
Bronze rattle (sistrum)
Length 22.3 cm
Naples Museum, inv. 109669
Found in the atrium of House I, 2, 10

The head consists of a broad strip of
bronze shaped into a loop and, strung
across it, four bronze rods, which are
looped over at the ends to hold them in
but are otherwise free to move to and fro,
giving a tinkling sound when shaken. On
the top of the loop is a figure of a cat with
a pine cone on her head and suckling two
kittens. The handle is plain. Though normally of bronze, silver *sistra* are known
(e.g., Naples, inv. 111770).

The *sistrum*, an instrument of Egyptian
origin, is one of the commonest symbols
of the worship of Isis, who took it over
from Hathor, the Egyptian goddess of
music. In sculpture and painting Isis normally holds a *sistrum* in her right hand
(see No. 191), and *sistra* were carried and
shaken by worshipers as part of the standard rituals of the cult, to repel the forces
of evil or to express joy or mourning.
Apuleius describes their use vividly in his
Metamorphoses (XI, 4).
Daremberg and Saglio, s.v. *Sistrum*.

187
Bronze rattle (sistrum)
Height 19 cm
Naples Museum, old inv. 2386
From Pompeii

A smaller version of No. 186. On the top
of the loop is the cat with kittens, and near
the base two small jackals; the ends of the
rods are shaped as ducks' heads. The
ornate handle incorporates two sacred
cobras and figures of Bes, Egyptian god of
the dance (cf. No. 179), and of Hathor,
goddess of music.

185

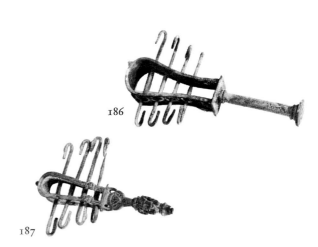
186

187

188
Pair of small bronze cymbals (cymbalum)
Diameter 11 cm
Naples Museum, inv. 76943
From Pompeii

Two circular sheets of bronze, each concave internally and surrounded by a broad flange, linked from the centers by a loose chain. Cymbals, usually portrayed in conjunction with tambourines (tympana) and pipes (see No. 310), were commonly played both at religious and at social functions (see also No. 193, group IX).

Daremberg and Saglio, s.v. Cymbalum; H. Hickmann, Annales du Service des Antiquités de l'Egypte 49 (1949) 451-545.

188

189
Bronze votive hand of Sabazius
Height 18 cm, width of base 8 cm
Naples Museum, inv. 5506
From Herculaneum, 8 February 1746

Sabazius was originally a Thracian or Phrygian divinity of vegetation, and in particular of barley and wheat. Known in Greece as early as the fifth century B.C., during the Roman Empire he was worshiped increasingly in a variety of syncretistic forms, most commonly as Zeus Sabazius or as Dionysus Sabazius, but also (just like Isis, see page 83) taking on the attributes of many other divinities.

One of the most striking features of his cult is a series of votive hands, of which the fingers form the gesture of benediction still familiar from the Latin Christian rite. Sabazius himself, bearded and wearing a tunic, trousers, and a Phrygian cap, is seated in the palm of the hand, his feet on a ram's head and his hands raised in the same characteristic gesture. Around him are his major attributes: on his right, curling up the back of the hand, his own serpent; on his left, the pine cone of Dionysus; and above him, the eagle of Zeus (of which only the claws now survive) grasping a thunderbolt. On the wrist is a curious, grotto-like frame enclosing the figures of a mother and child. Elsewhere on the hand are shown a scarab, two cymbals, a double flute (Phrygian pipes), a winged staff of Mercury (caduceus), a pair of scales, an owl, a lizard, a frog, a tortoise, a wine bowl (crater), a flaming altar, a whip, and a little table with another pine cone.

Two very similar hands were found at Pompeii in 1954, in a shop (II, 1, 12) identified by the excavators as that of a dealer in small religious and magical objects.

C. Blinkenberg, Archaeologische Studien (Copenhagen & Leipzig 1904) 75, no. E13;

189

O. Elia "Vasi magici e mani pantee a Pompei," RAAN XXXV (1960) 7ff.; E. Lane, "Two Votive Hands in Missouri," Muse 4 (1970) 43-48.

190
Architectural landscape with figures
Length 36 cm, height 37 cm
Naples Museum, inv. 9475
Found in the Temple of Isis, 1776

One of a series of idealized landscapes, found on the walls of the portico enclosing the main precinct. The landscapes occupied the centers of large monochrome panels within the composition, alternating in this position with representations of priests and of other ceremonial attendants of the goddess (see also No. 178). They follow the familiar "sacro-idyllic" conventions, but most of them include elements that would have been recognizably Egyptian in intention: in this instance the tall tower with curving "horns," which may be compared with an altar, and which may represent a tomb.

Elia, Mon Pitt 12; Rostowzew, "Architekturlandschaft" 79, no. 3.

190

191
Statue of Isis in Archaic style
Pentelic marble
Height of statue 1.06 m, height of base 95 cm
Naples Museum, inv. 976
From the northwest corner of the colonnade in the Temple of Isis

The goddess' hair is dressed in an elaborate Archaic Greek style, with a garland of five rosettes. She wears a long, clinging tunic in fine material, held tight under her breasts with a belt the clasp of which is formed of two snakes' heads. Over her shoulders, making sleeves, is an equally thin shawl, tucked into the belt. In her right hand she held a sistrum, of which only the handle remains; from her left dangles an ankh, the Egyptian symbol of life. When found, the statue was rich in traces of its original coloring, with remains of gilding on the hair, rosettes, the collar and hem of her tunic, and the snake bracelets on her wrists. She has heavy red eyebrows and pupils, and there are traces of red also on the tree stump beside her left leg and among the folds around the hem of her tunic.

She stands on her original base, which bears the dedicatory inscription: L. Caecilius Phoebus posuit l[oco] d[ato] d[ecurionum] d[ecreto]. "Lucius Caecilius Phoebus set [this statue] up in a place granted by decree of the town council"; it is one of many indications that this temple was official municipal property. L. Caecilius Phoebus was a freedman of the rich Pompeian banking family. The statue is the only complete figure of Isis found in the temple. Of two others, composite works in wood and marble, only fragments of the marble part survive.

Mau-Kelsey 170; Tran tam Tinh, Pompéi 156, no. 81; Reuterswaard, Polychromie 186f.; CIL X, 849.

192 (color plate, vol. I, p. 67)
Wall painting: Dionysiac cult objects
Height 46 cm, width 46 cm
Naples Museum, inv. 8795
From Pompeii

Along a narrow ledge at the top of a small flight of steps are, from left to right: a tambourine; a wicker basket, on which are a drinking horn draped with a panther skin, a drinking cup, and a thyrsus; and a second, taller drinking cup decorated with vine leaves. On the steps are a spray of bay, a pair of cymbals, and a small panther grappling with a snake. All these objects are associated with the cult of Dionysus. The picture, which appears to come from the middle zone of a Fourth Style monumental composition, is one of several in the Naples Museum portraying attributes of various gods, all of which may have come from the same decorative scheme.

MB 5 (Rome 1841) pl. LVIII.

192

193 (see illus. p. 179)
Painted frieze from the Hall of the Mysteries (reproduction)
Lent by Imperial Tobacco Limited
Original at Pompeii, Villa of the Mysteries

The Villa of the Mysteries was a wealthy suburban residence (*villa urbana*), built toward the middle of the second century B.C. a short distance outside the walls, between the two roads that converge on the Herculaneum Gate. It was extensively remodeled, modernized, and redecorated about 60 B.C. During the last years of the town, after the earthquake, parts of it continued to be used as the center of a farming property under the charge of a steward, who was a freedman of the old Samnite family of the Istacidii, but (just as at Oplontis, see No. 327) the residence, with its magnificent series of early Second Style paintings lay empty. Who the owner responsible for these paintings was we do not know.

The so-called Hall of the Mysteries lay near the southwest corner of the building, entered by a large door in the west wall and with a large window in the middle of the south wall, looking out across a portico toward the Bay of Naples. The walls were covered with nearly lifesize figures, arranged like a frieze against the background of what was still in effect a First Style wall scheme. This background was already in place when the figures were painted, though whether this means that the figures were an afterthought, added at a slightly later date, or whether this sequence merely represents the way the artist chose to lay out and execute his composition, we have no means of telling.

Ever since the discovery of these paintings in 1929-30, their significance has been the subject of lively debate. The suggestion that this was a hall in which the Dionysiac Mysteries were actually celebrated can certainly be excluded. The essence of the Mysteries was that they were secrets, to be guarded jealously from profane eyes, not openly displayed where any passer-by could see them. On the other hand, the paintings are shot through and through with Dionysiac imagery; they reflect in intimate detail the world of ideas to which an initiate of the Mysteries belonged. Side by side with the gods and their attendant train of satyrs, maenads, and other Dionysiac followers, there is also a continuous thread of strictly human action, and it is a striking fact that at this human level the small boy reading from a scroll is the only male figure present. This is a women's world, and according to one widely held interpretation the whole cycle portrays and symbolizes the ceremonies and rituals prior to the wedding of a human bride. There is room for discussion how far one can distinguish the actual physical ceremonials of marriage from portrayals of the symbolic rituals of mystic marriage with the godhead—if indeed the two were clearly distinguishable. But, on this interpretation, the overall intent seems to be clear enough.

191

There seems to be fairly general agreement that both in its broad conception and in much of its detail the frieze derives from a Hellenistic model or models and is thus at one remove a unique representation of the lost world of Greek lifesize figured painting (*megalographia*). How closely it followed its sources is open to discussion. It would be pressing coincidence too far to imagine that the available wall space was exactly the same in both cases; and the fact the frieze falls into a number of distinct compositional groups (some of which, such as that of Dionysus and Ariadne [VI], are known from other replicas) would have allowed for a measure of rearrangement, omission, or addition. The fact that, despite the unifying hand of the Campanian copyist, one can detect models that were ultimately of different styles and dates, is not in itself significant. Some such assimilation could well have taken place already in the Hellenistic sources. On balance, it seems likely that the relationship between model and copy was a close one but that, as was customary in ancient copying, the process was one of adjustment and adaptation rather than of slavish imitation.

The interpretation that follows, though not free from problems and uncertainties, does offer a plausible and consistent account of these remarkable paintings. It reads from left to right round the room, starting from the small doorway at the northwest corner.

I. Entry of the bride for her initiation. A nude boy reads out a sacred text under the guidance of a woman with a scroll and a writing stylus in her hand. A wreathed attendant, bearing an olive branch, carries in a silver platter of cakes.

II. Preparations for sacrifice. A seated priestess removes a cloth from a basket carried by an attendant, while another attendant pours purifying water on her right hand.

III. The scene shifts to a supranatural level dominated by the figures of Dionysus and Ariadne in the middle of the east wall. An elderly Silenus plays his lyre, resting it on a column. A youthful satyr and his female counterpart are seated on a rock, he playing the panpipes, she suckling a she-goat.

IV. A woman in an attitude of startled alarm, left hand raised as if to ward off the influence of the scenes that follow on the east wall. This figure cleverly links the two walls, gazing across the corner of the room to bind the two together.

V. A young satyr gazes into a bowl held up before him by an elderly Silenus, while a second young satyr holds up a theatrical mask. The precise meaning is doubtful, but gazing into bowls was a well-known form of divination.

VI. Central to the east wall, dominating the room, Dionysus reclines in the lap of an enthroned Ariadne.

VII. A kneeling woman, with a long torch over her shoulder, reaches out to unveil an object that is almost certainly to be identified as a huge ritual phallus. On the ground lies a winnowing basket. Two women look on.

VIII. A female figure, with dark wings spread, holds up her left hand as if to shut out the previous scene and raises her right, to strike with a whip the kneeling figure of scene IX. Like figure IV, this winged figure, though compositionally part of the previous group of scenes, really belongs with the next group, linking the two walls across the angle of the room.

IX. A half-naked girl kneels, burying her face in the lap of a seated woman, who helps to bare her back to the ritual flagellation inflicted by the winged figure. On their right are two women. One, fully clothed, brings forward a *thyrsus,* the wand of Dionysus and his followers; the other, naked, dances in ecstasy, clashing a pair of cymbals.

X. The bride's toilet. An attendant helps her to dress her hair. A winged Eros holds up a mirror.

XI. Once again the scene is completed across the corner of the room. A second Eros leans on a pillar gazing up at the bride.

XII. The bride, robed and veiled, sits on the marriage couch. On her fourth finger she displays her wedding ring.

A. Maiuri, *La Villa dei Misteri* (Rome, 1931); O. Brendel, *JdAI* 81 (1966) 206ff.; Kraus and von Matt, 93-96, whose interpretation we follow. For a totally different interpretation see *Guida Archeologica di Pompei*, ed. F. Coarelli (Verona 1976) 340-346.

194

Inscribed marble slab recording a dedication by the Ministri Fortunae Augustae
Height 70 cm, length 47 cm
Naples Museum, inv. 76/248
Found loose in the Basilica, 1884

L[ucius] Numisius Primus L[ucius] Numisius Optatus L[ucius] Melissaeus Plocamus ministr[i] Fortun[ae] Aug[ustae] ex d[ecreto] d[ecurionum] iussu L[ucii] Iuli[i] Pontici [et] P[ublii] Gavi[i] Pastoris d[uo] v[iri] i[ure] d[icundo et] Q[uinti] Poppaei [et] C[aii] Vibi[i] aedil[um] Q[uinto] Futio [et] P[ublio] Calvisio co[n] s[ulibus].
"Lucius Numisius Primus, Lucius Numisius Optatus and Lucius Melissaeus Plocamus, ministers of the cult of Fortuna Augusta, [made this dedication] in accordance with the decree of the decurions, on the instruction of Lucius Julius Ponticus and Publius Gavius Pastor, chief magistrates, and of Quintus Poppaeus and Caius Vibius, aediles, during the consulship of Quintus Futius and Publius Calvisius."

The cult of Fortuna Augusta, i.e., of the prosperity of the emperor, was established at Pompeii by Marcus Tullius, a prominent citizen who had been a chief magistrate *(duovir)* and who built a temple of this dedication shortly before A.D. 3. Although the dedicators named in this inscription were all freedmen of wealthy Pompeian families, the body of *ministri* might also include slaves. It seems to have been the practice of this body to dedicate a new statue shortly after the accession of each new emperor. The pair of Roman consuls named here is not recorded elsewhere, but the inscription is probably to be dated to the reign of Caligula, *c.* A.D. 39-40.
CIL x. 187; *ILS* 6384; Castrén 76-78.

195

Inscribed slab recording a dedication by the Ministri Augusti
Marble, restored from four pieces
Length 37.5 cm, height 31 cm
Naples Museum, inv. 3794
Pompeii, find-spot not known

Narcissus Popidi Moschi [servus et] Nymphodotus Capras[ii] Iucundi [servus] min[istri] Aug[usti] d[ecurionum] d[ecreto] iussu P[ublii] Vetti[i] Celeris D[ecimi] Alfidi[i].
"Narcissus, slave of Popidius Moschus, and Nymphodotus, slave of Caprasius Jucundus, ministers of the cult of Augustus, [made this dedication] by decree of the decurions, on the instructions of Publius Vettius Celer and Decimus Alfidius."

Members of the college of *ministri Augusti* held office for one year, and membership was open to slaves as well as freedmen. Dedications such as this one seem to have marked important events within the Imperial family. The first

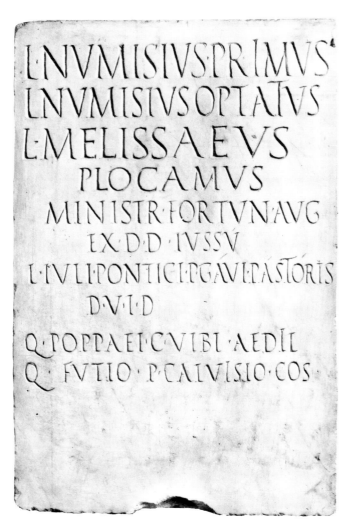

L·NVMISIVS·PRIMVS
L·NVMISIVS·OPTATVS
L·MELISSAEVS
PLOCAMVS
MINISTRI·FORTVN·AVG
EX·D·D·IVSSV
L·IVLI·PONTICI·P·GAVI·PASTORIS
D·V·I·D
Q·POPPAEI·C·VIBI·AEDIL
Q·FVTIO·P·CATVISIO·COS·

194

196

NARCISSVS·POPIDI
MOSCHI
NYMPHODOTVS·CAPRA
IVCVNDI
MIN·AVG   D·IVSSV
T·VETTI·CELERIS·D·ALFIDI

195

record of the college dates from 2 B.C.
(*CIL* X. 890), when one of the *ministri*
was Numisius Popidius Moschus, a freedman of the influential Popidius family.
The subsequent election to the college
of one of his own slaves, Narcissus,
illustrates very clearly the network of
patronage to which the service of the
Imperial cult gave rise. This inscription
must date from the early years of the first
century A.D.
CIL X. 908; Castrén 75.

196
Wall painting: figure of a priestess
Height 95 cm, width 43 cm
Naples Museum, inv. 8903
From Herculaneum

The fragment, and its companion piece
showing a youth carrying a stool (Naples
Museum, inv. 9374), were probably cut
from the architectural framework of a
Fourth Style scheme. The woman is veiled
and carries an incense box on a tray in
her left hand.
Helbig no. 1795; cf. *Pitture di Ercolano* IV,
5, pl. 1.

197
Wall painting of Mercury
Height 73 cm, width 49 cm
Naples Museum, inv. 9452
From Pompeii

The youthful god, who was patron of
commerce as well as messenger of the
gods, is shown with wings at his temples
and his ankles and bearing his symbolic
staff, or *caduceus* (see No. 216) in his left
hand. In his right hand, instead of the
usual money bag, he carries what may be
a fish trap, and beside his right foot is a
small tortoise (or turtle). The most likely
position for such a painting would be in a
household shrine or on the outer wall of
a shop, belonging to somebody who was
connected with fishing or the sale of fish
products.

Helbig 358; *Pitture di Ercolano* v, 89, pl. XIX.

199

197

198
Bronze brazier on three legs
Height 78 cm
Naples Museum, inv. 1572
From one of the sites in the Vesuvius area

The bowl, which is removable for
emptying, rests on a three-legged stand
on animal's-paw feet and is strengthened
with bronze hoops, a rigid version of the
collapsible tripods such as No. 138. The
distinctive shape, in a more ornate
version, the so-called Delphic tripod,
appears frequently in the late Second Style
paintings, as on the wall at Oplontis
(No. 327).

199 (color plate, vol. I, pp. 72-73)
**Wall painting from a household shrine
(lararium)**
Width 1.83 m, height 1.28 m
Naples Museum, inv. 8905
Found in VIII, insula 2 or 3, 6 June 1761

The painting is divided into two registers.
In the upper register, below three garlands, is a scene of sacrifice. The *genius*,
or presiding divinity of the household,
with head veiled and bearing a cornucopia, symbolic of plenty, holds out a
dish *(patera)* over a marble altar. He is
attended by a small boy carrying a fillet
(a wreath, with ribbons for tying) and a
platter; opposite him a musician plays the
double pipes, beating time with a wooden
clapper beneath his left foot, while a slave
brings forward a pig for sacrifice (see No.
200). On either side stand the two Lares
of the household, pouring wine from a
drinking horn, or *rhyton,* into a small
wine bucket, or *situla.* In the lower
register two serpents approach the offerings (of fruit?) upon an altar. Together
with the setting of rich vegetation, they
symbolize the fertility of nature and the
bounty of the earth beneath.

PAH I, 133; *MB* 9 (Rome 1845) 161, pl. XXVII.

198

201

202

200
Small bronze pig on a rectangular stand
Length 13.5 cm, height 11.5 cm
Naples Museum, inv. 4905
From Herculaneum

Hollow cast, the details sharpened with a chisel after casting. It is mounted on its original base, which stands on four splayed cloven hooves springing from formal, palmette designs. On the pig's left flank are inscribed the letters *HER. VOE. M.L.* No satisfactory interpretation of this abbreviated text has been proposed. The prominent position of the letters *HER* suggests the possibility of a dedication to Hercules, to whom a pig was the customary animal of sacrifice. The figure would in that case have been placed in a household shrine *(lararium)*.
Bronzi di Ercolano 1, 83 and 279.

200

201
Miniature bronze altar
Height 11 cm, length 19 cm, width 15 cm
Naples Museum, inv. 74001
From Pompeii

The rectangular box in which the offering was burnt is decorated with simple profiled moldings and with crenellations. It stands on four legs, with wings at the junction with the body and ending in animal's cloven hooves. The form is also found on a much larger scale used as a brazier (e.g., Naples Museum, inv. 73005).

Little altars were part of the equipment of a household shrine *(lararium)*. They were normally built in or made of terracotta, only rarely of bronze.
Boyce 16; Gusman 134.

202
Miniature bronze altar
Height 13 cm, diameter 15 cm
Naples Museum, inv. 73997
From Pompeii

Beneath a line of tiny crenellations, engraved with a T-shaped design, alternately upright and inverted, the circular drum is ornamented with moldings of an architec-

tural character. It stands on three lion's-paw feet, the shafts of which splay out into forms that are based on the elements of an Ionic capital. Like No. 201, this altar is a miniature version of a shape used also for braziers (e.g., Naples Museum, inv. 73012) and would have been made for use in a *lararium*.
MB 3 (Rome 1839) pl. XXXII.

203

204

203
Bronze statuette of Bacchus
Height 34.8 cm (40 cm with base)
Naples Museum, inv. 5009
From Herculaneum

The vine-crowned young god of wine holds a pine-cone-topped staff *(thyrsus)* in his left hand and once tipped up a drinking cup *(cantharus)* in his raised right. The slender forms of the figure suggest that the original of this bronze goes back through the age of Julius Caesar and Sulla ultimately to the tradition of Praxiteles in the late fourth century B.C. Such household gods gave Romans around the Bay of Naples a very distant view of the great epochs of Greek art.
Chiurazzi 65, no. 98.

204
Bronze statuette of Hercules
Height 21 cm
Naples Museum, inv. 5780
From Herculaneum

The drunken Hercules is shown nude, with a beard, his club over his right shoulder and his left hand probably holding a drinking cup, now lost. The statuette is of good workmanship, and the molded base, which does not belong to the statuette, is finely decorated.

205

206

Bronze tintinnabulum in the form of a gladiator; four of the five original bells preserved
Height of figure 21 cm
Naples Museum, inv. 27853
Found in Herculaneum, 8 February 1740

These fanciful combinations of bells and phallus, intended to ward off evil spirits, at times take on a remarkable complexity. Here a gladiator armed with a knife and with a protective leather strap wrapped around his left arm attacks his own phallus, which turns into the foreparts of a panther.
Grant, De Simone, and Merella 138, 143.

207

Pottery lamp in the form of a figure of Priapus
Height 14 cm, length 11.5 cm
Naples Museum, inv. 27869
From Pompeii

The little rustic god of fruitfulness, protector of flocks, bees, vineyards, and market gardens, son of Dionysus and Aphrodite, is modeled as a lamp, provided with a ring for suspension, and probably hung from the lintel of an entrance doorway to bring good luck and to ward off evil spirits.
Fiorelli, *Raccolta pornografica* no. 201.

206

205

Bronze tintinnabulum with three hanging bells
Length 11.5 cm
Naples Museum, inv. 27837
From Herculaneum

Tintinnabula (tinkling bells of the type used also in some forms of dancing) were hung in the doorways of houses and shops, often together with a lamp, as a protection against evil spirits. This elaborately and aggressively male object, equipped with wings and the hind legs of a lion, was a symbol of plenty as well as a deterrent to evil spirits, and as such it was a favorite component of such bells. It is also found, used with the same intent, on terracotta plaques let into the outer walls of buildings, particularly at street corners (see page 64).
Grant, De Simone, and Merella 140, illus.; cf. Col. Famin, *Musée Royal de Naples: peintures, bronzes et statues erotiques du cabinet secret* (Paris 1857) 29f., pls. XXIV, XXVII, and XXVIII.

207

208 (color plate, vol. I, p. 65)
Statuette of Aphrodite with Priapus
Fine white, translucent marble, possibly
from Paros
Height 62 cm
Naples Museum, inv. 152798
Found on a table in the *tablinum* of House
II, 4, 6

The group represents Aphrodite preparing to bathe (see No. 209), raising her left
foot to remove her sandal and resting her
left forearm on the head of a small figure
of the god Priapus; a tiny Eros sits below
her foot. Aphrodite's left hand, now missing, was carved in a separate piece of
marble. The group is remarkable for the
extensive remains of gilding as well as
some traces of paint. In addition to her
necklace, armbands, a bracelet, and gilded
sandals, Aphrodite wears an exiguous,
bikini-like harness. Her eyes are inlaid

with cement and glass paste. The hair and
pubic hair of both main figures were once
gilded (the dark red paint now visible was
the underlay), and there are traces of red
paint on the lips of the goddess and on the
tree stump that supports the group; of
green on Priapus' pedestal; and of black
on the base.

The statuette was found in the large
complex of rented accommodation, including a bath-house and tavern, known
as the villa of Julia Felix. *Graffiti* and
other finds suggest that this part of the
complex may have served as a brothel in
the last years of the town's history.
Reuterswaard, *Polychromie* 184f.; *BJb* 170
(1970) 142, M50.

209
Bronze statuette of Aphrodite
Height 17.5 cm
Naples Museum, inv. 5133
Found in Herculaneum, 22 February 1757

The figure belongs to a large series of representations of Aphrodite (Venus) preparing to bathe (cf. No. 208). She is taking off
her left sandal, supporting herself against
a narrow tree trunk, around which is
curled a dolphin, one of her many characteristic attributes. Her armbands and
anklets are made of gold, and the palmette-
and-scrollwork decoration on the base is
inlaid in silver.
Bronzi di Ercolano 2, 53f., pl. XIV.

209

210
**Replica of the household shrine (lararium)
in the House of the Gilded Amorini** (VI,
16, 7) (not illustrated)
Lent by Imperial Tobacco Limited
Height 2.07 m, width 1.25 m, depth 74 cm

This *lararium,* the lower part of which
was built of rubble faced with plaster and
painted to represent colored marble veneer, and the upper part constructed of
wood and painted stucco and supported
on two fluted colonnettes of greenish *cipollino* marble, stood against the north
wall of the peristyle. A *lararium* was es-
sentially the shrine of the Lares, the
protecting divinities of the house (see
No. 199), who figured in it in association
with whatever other divinities the family
held in special honor. Within it the master
of the house would make small daily offerings, and it was the scene of ceremonial
offerings on important family occasions.

The group here displayed (Jupiter,
Minerva, Mercury, two Lares, and a
lamp), with the exception of the figure of
Jupiter, is not that actually found in this
particular *lararium;* though absolutely
characteristic, it is a composite group,
made up from other *lararia.* The *lararium*
in the House of the Gilded Amorini contained (along the upper ledge) Jupiter
(No. 215) flanked by the other members of
the Capitoline triad, Juno and Minerva,
and accompanied by Mercury (Hermes;
cf. No. 197), the patron god of commerce,
who was very popular in this context, and
(on the lower ledge) two Lares and a
bronze vessel.
NSc 1907, 565-571; Boyce 57, no. 221.

208

152798

211

211
Bronze lamp in the shape of a duck
Height 8 cm, length 13.5 cm
Naples Museum, inv. 110674
From Pompeii, 3 March 1875

The body of the duck is hollow, forming the reservoir, with a hole for filling in the middle of the back. The tail constitutes the nozzle, and the head looks backward to form the handle. The legs are indicated in shallow relief, tucked up below the wings.

212
Bronze statuette of Minerva
Height 20 cm (25 cm with base)
Naples Museum, inv. 5288
From Herculaneum

With her crested helmet, *aegis* (goatskin mantle with Medusa's head and snaky locks), libation dish, and spear, the goddess of wisdom and industry is based on famous cult-statues of the fifth century B.C. The style is designed to recall the Athenian statues of about 460 B.C., the generation before Pheidias, but the mixture of elements in dress and secondary details indicates the model for this statuette belonged to the eclectic age of Julius Caesar or Augustus. The Minerva was doubtless one of a group of Olympians and other divinities (like Isis-Fortuna, No. 181, or Bacchus, No. 203) in a household shrine *(lararium)* or on the sideboard of a private room. Alternate rows of scales in her *aegis* are gilded.
Chiurazzi 78, no. 123.

213
Bronze statuette of a Lar
Height 29 cm
Naples Museum, inv. 5424
Found at Herculaneum in April 1762, near the theater

The Lares, originally Etruscan divinities of locality, in Roman times were worshiped as protectors of the house, usually placed in pairs within the household shrine *(lararium;* see No. 210) on either side of the figures of whatever other gods were specially favored by the family. They are regularly portrayed as youthful figures, wearing short-sleeved tunics and mantles, often with skirts swirling in the dance. This example carries a sacrificial dish and a cornucopia, or horn of plenty.
Bronzi di Ercolano 2, 197, pl. LII; cf. *Antike Welt* 6 no. 4 (1975) 26f.

214
Bronze statuette of a Lar
Height 27 cm
Naples Museum, inv. 5427
Found in the earliest excavations at Herculaneum

Figure similar to No. 213 but in a more restrained pose. He carries a wine bucket *(situla)* and waves a sheaf of wheat.
Bronzi di Ercolano 2, 213, pl. LVI; *MB* 8 (Rome 1844) pl. LXXIII.

215
Bronze statuette of Jupiter
Height 16.5 cm
Naples Museum, inv. 133323
From the *lararium* in the peristyle of the House of the Gilded Amorini (VI, 16, 7)

This figure of Jupiter sat, enthroned, on the upper shelf of the *lararium* (see No. 210) together with the other members of the Capitoline triad, Juno and Minerva, and with Mercury, the patron of commerce. Jupiter is bearded, the upper part of his body naked, the lower half wrapped in a mantle. In his right hand is a thunderbolt, and the left probably held a scepter, now missing.
Boyce 57, no. 221; *NSc* 1907, 565-571.

213

212

214

216
Bronze statuette of Mercury
Height 19 cm
Naples Museum, inv. 115553
From Pompeii, 15 January 1887

Mercury, the Greek Hermes, messenger of
the gods and patron god of commerce,
stands on a circular, molded pedestal,
with his cloak draped over his left shoulder, wearing his characteristic winged hat
(petasos) and with wings at his ankles. In
his right hand he holds a money bag, and
in his left a winged staff *(caduceus)* consisting of two intertwined serpents. Probably from a *lararium.*

217 (color plate, vol. 1, p. 14)
**Wall painting: sacro-idyllic landscape
with shepherd and goats**
Height 50 cm, width 49 cm
Naples Museum, inv. 9418
From Pompeii, exact location unknown

Landscape from the center of a wall panel,
probably of the Fourth Style. It portrays
an idealized rustic shrine, set within a
rocky landscape with trees. In the foreground a man is pushing a goat toward
the shrine, as if for sacrifice. On a rock to
the right stands a shepherd, and on another rock, to the left, two more figures,
one of them a statue.

Rostowzew, "Architekturlandschaft" 87;
Peters 148; *Pitture di Ercolano* 2, 151.

217

215

216

191

VI Trade and Occupations

218
Inscribed marble slab advertising the Baths of M. Crassus Frugi
Length 1.15 m, height 57 cm
Naples Museum, inv. 3829
Found in 1749, reused as a shelf within a shrine just outside the Herculaneum Gate

Thermae M[arci] Crassi Frugi aqua marina et baln[eum] aqua dulci Ianuarius l[ibertus]. "The Baths of Marcus Crassus Frugi. Sea water and fresh water bathing. Januarius, freedman."

These baths must have been located near the sea shore, probably on the promontory that in antiquity marked the west side of the mouth of the river Sarno, and that is known to have contained thermal springs. The owner was presumably the consul of A.D. 64, who died a few years later and who is known to have owned another comparable bathing establishment near Baiae (Pliny, *Nat. Hist.* XXXI. 5). This inscription, the first to be found by the eighteenth-century excavators, is best interpreted as a roadside advertisement for the baths, set up by the freedman who had charge of them.

CIL X. 1063; *ILS* 5724; A. Maiuri, *RAAN* n.s. XXXIV (1959) 73–79; D'Arms 214–215.

219
Inscribed limestone slab recording the modernization of the Stabian Baths
Length 84 cm, height 44 cm
Naples Museum, inv. 3826
Found in 1857 in the Stabian Baths

C[aius] Vulius C[aii] f[ilius] P[ublius] Aninius C[aii] f[ilius] IIv[iri] i[ure] d[icundo] laconicum et destrictarium faciund[a] et porticus et palaestr[am] reficiunda locarunt ex d[ecurionum] d[ecreto] ex ea pequnia quod eos e lege in ludos aut in monumento consumere oportuit faciun[da] coerarunt eidemque probaru[nt].

"Caius Uulius, son of Caius, and Publius Aninius, son of Caius, chief magistrates, put out to contract the construction of a sweating room (*laconicum*) and a scraping room (*destrictarium*) and the reconstruction of the porticoes and the exercise yard (*palaestra*). [This they did] in accordance with the decree of the decurions, out of the money that they were by law due to spend on games or public building. They had charge of the work and they approved it."

218

219

The *laconicum* was a room for sweating under conditions of intense dry heat, and it can be identified with certainty as the still-extant circular room with a conical vault, which was later converted into a *frigidarium*. The *destrictarium*, for cleaning off the oil and dirt accumulated during exercise, which one did with a strigil (No. 220), lay to the north of the *laconicum* and was later eliminated. The porticoes were those of the present *palaestra*. The modernization of the Stabian Baths was undertaken quite soon after the foundation of the colony in 80 B.C., and the magistrates in charge of the work were both probably among the original colonists.

CIL X. 829; *ILS* 5706; H. Eschebach, *RM* 80 (1973) 235–242.

220, 221
Strigil and oil flask
Bronze
Length of strigil 23 cm
Naples Museum, inv. 70079 (strigil), 69970, 69927 (oil flask and stopper)
From one of the sites in the Vesuvius area

Before the introduction of fat-based soaps in the late Empire, the cleansing medium used by athletes in the *palaestra* and by bathers of both sexes was a mixture of low-grade olive oil and pumice. This was applied to the body and then scraped off by means of a long, narrow, scoop-like scraper, or strigil. A common form of public benefaction was money for a free distribution of such oil. Sets of strigils, often together with a small oil flask, or *aryballos,* are commonly found attached to a loop that went round the wrist for convenience in carrying.

Daremberg and Saglio, s.v. *Strigilis.*

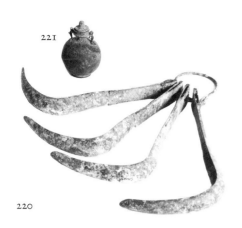

221

220

complete set contained fourteen such pieces, numbered serially. But the discovery in Athens in 1886 of a set of nine similar pieces, numbered I, III, VI, VII, VIII (two examples), X, XII, and found together with a silver gaming board of a scalloped circular design with twelve points, may indicate a variant using only twelve pieces.

A set of six comparable pieces, shaped like boars and numbered I, II, VI, VII, VIII, IX, was found in 1937 in a house at Herculaneum, in a wooden box.

M. Laurent, "Tessères en os du Musée d'Athènes," *Le Musée Belge* VII (1903) 83ff.

224
Four knucklebone gaming pieces
Naples Museum, inv. 76972, 76981, 76987, 76990
From Pompeii

Knucklebones, a traditional game already popular in classical Greece, was played with a set of four pieces *(tali)*, either *astragali* of sheep or goats or pieces made from terracotta, glass, bronze, or precious materials to the same conventional shape. The pieces were oblong and rounded at the ends, with two wider and two narrower long sides, each of which presented a recognizably different surface and had a different value (1, 3, 4, and 6) and name. There were many variants of the game, but in its simplest and commonest form each player threw the four *tali*, scoring according to the value of the long sides that fell uppermost, not on a simple numerical basis but, as in poker or poker dice, in accordance with certain combinations of numbers. The top throw, a "Venus" or a "Royal" *(basileus)*, consisted of four faces all different, and the lowest throw, "The Dogs" or "Four Vultures," of four plain faces (1); another poor throw was the *senio*, some combination unknown of the twisted face (6) and three other faces. In a version played by the emperor Augustus (Suetonius, *Life of Augustus* 71, 2) any player throwing "The Dogs" or a *senio* put 4 denarii (small coins) into the pool, which was scooped by the first player to throw a "Venus."

J. P. V. D. Balsdon, *Life and Leisure in Ancient Rome* (New York 1969) 155.

225
Four ivory dice
a. Cube 1.2 cm
Naples Museum, old inv. 552
From the Vesuvius area
b. Cube 2.1 cm
Naples Museum, inv. 115530
From Pompeii VIII
c. Cube 1.3 cm
Naples Museum, inv. 116480
From the entrance to IX, 7, 4, one of a pair
d. Cube 1.4 cm
Naples Museum, inv. 119371
From a tavern, VII, 15, 4, one of a pair

Roman dice *(tesserae)*, like modern dice, were small cubes with the values 1–6 in groups of dots or letters on the six faces so arranged that two opposing faces always added up to seven. The Greeks usually played with three dice, but by the beginning of the Empire the Romans started to use only two, shaken in a little cup, although they continued to use three for board games such as *duodecim scripta*. There were probably names for all the different combinations, as in knucklebones (see No. 224).

J. P. V. D. Balsdon, *Life and Leisure in Ancient Rome* (New York 1969) 156.

226
Cicada in rock crystal
Length 6 cm
Naples Museum, inv. 109629
From House I, 2, 3, found 12 April 1873

Found together with a small crystal duck, a small crystal amphora, and a faceted lump of crystal, in the *tablinum*. Rock crystal, of which the best quality came from India, was prized for its rarity. Other recurrent subjects were fish, shells, walnuts, and small vases. It is not known whether these were simply collected as *objets d'art*, given as New Year's presents like Nos. 288-291, had a funerary significance (*Gnomon* 1976, 519), or whether some were also used as gaming pieces.

Bull Inst XLVI (1874), 202f.; cf. *BMC Gems* nos. 3971-3985.

222

222
Three glass unguentaria (perfume flasks)
Heights 9.5 cm, 8.6 cm, 8.5 cm
Naples Museum, inv. 114890, 12062, 12392
From Pompeii; 114890 from the *tablinum* of IX, 6, 5 with several toilet articles, including No. 59

All free blown, such little flasks were among the first articles mass-produced in blown glass, and were sold with their contents. Their forms are so varied that it seems that the different shapes were the trade marks of specific types of oils, ointments, or perfumes. Later first century A.D.

Isings 40, form 26, and 42, form 28a.

223
Three bone gaming pieces
a. Black; on the reverse the number IIII
b. White; on the reverse the number IIII
c. White; on the reverse the number XI
Lengths 4.5 cm, 5.1 cm, and 5 cm respectively
Naples Museum, inv. 109837, 109848, 109854
From Pompeii

The shape may represent a trussed fowl. Piece *a* was found together with ten others of the same form, bearing the numbers I, II, III, VII, VIII, X, XI, XIII, XIV. Pieces *b* and *c* were found together with eight others, numbered I, II, III, V, VII, VIII, IX, X. This suggests that in one form of the game a

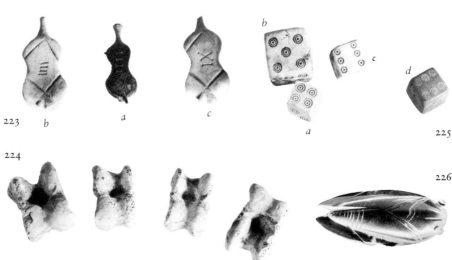

223 *b* *a* *c*

224

225

226

227a
Bone tally piece from a board game
Diameter 3.3 cm
Naples Museum, inv. 77104
From Pompeii

On one side is a hand, palm forward, with the thumb and forefinger touching to form a ring and the other three fingers clenched. On the reverse, in Roman numerals, "XIII." There are several other versions, with different arrangements of the fingers, among the Naples Museum collections (e.g., inv. 77127, 109864). Each side appears to have a different significance, as the numbers on the back (none higher than XXV) bear no relation to the numbers indicated by the fingers on the front. Such pieces may have served as score-counters in some board game.

CIL X. 2. 8069. 101; Henzen, *Annali dell' Inst* XX (1848) 282.

227b
Four bone gaming counters
a. Obverse: a female head in profile
Reverse: IIII/ΛIBIA (= Livia)/Δ
Diameter 3.3 cm
Naples Museum, inv. 77129
From the Vesuvius area
CIL X. 2. 8069. 9.

a　　　　　*b*

b. Obverse: façade of a building with a statue in a large niche
Reverse: II/ΕΥΡΟΛΟΧΟΥ (= *Euro-lochou*)/B
There was a village called Eurylochos near Alexandria
Diameter 3.0 cm
Naples Museum, inv. 109586
From Pompeii, 9 April 1863, "Portico del passetto pensile"
CIL X. 2. 8069. 8.

c　　　　　*d*

c. Obverse: seated figure of a woman, her chin resting on the knuckles of her left hand
Reverse: II/ΦΥΛIC (= *Phylis*)/B
Diameter 3.2 cm
Naples Museum, inv. 119383
From Pompeii I, 1, 6, 31 August 1874

d. Obverse: head of a youth in profile with a fillet in his hair
Reverse: XIII/ΕΡΛΛΗC (= Hermes)/IΓ
Diameter 3.5 cm
Naples Museum, inv. 120299
From the peristyle of V, 4, 1, 9 October 1890

The Romans were enthusiastic players of board games; we find improvised boards scratched on the pavements of public buildings throughout the Empire. Of the two most popular games, *duodecim scripta* and *latrunculi,* there is enough evidence from ancient authors to reconstruct in broad terms how they were played. But of others we know very little, beyond the gaming pieces (e.g., No. 223). The four counters exhibited here belong to a board game, possibly invented in Alexandria in the early Empire, which involved sets of fifteen counters variously carved on one side with the heads or busts of gods and goddesses *(d),* the Imperial family *(a),* famous athletes, caricatured mythological figures *(c),* views of buildings in Alexandria *(b),* and victory crowns from ancient games. On the reverse is an inscription in Greek identifying the design on the front. Above the inscription is a number in Roman numerals (from I to XV), and below it, its equivalent in Greek (A to IΓ). The heads and busts greatly outnumber the buildings and crowns, which must have had a special significance. A set from a child's tomb in Kertch comprised 12 heads or busts, 1 building, and 2 crowns.

Rostovzeff, *Rev Arch* IV Ser. V (1905) 113.

228
Wall painting: bakery
Width 52.5 cm, height 61.4 cm
Naples Museum, inv. 9071
From the *tablinum* of House VII, 3, 30

The setting is the front room of a baker's shop, where a baker, dressed with surprising formality and seated in a dignified position, is handing out loaves of bread to three eager-looking customers. Most of the loaves are round and puffy, and scored before baking into wedge-shaped divisions. Loaves of this form have been found at Pompeii. This was the standard variety, but the baker shown here has other kinds as well, rolls in a basket and a pile of sliced or ring-shaped bread at one corner of the shelf behind him. The painter's style is lively and straightforward, interesting because he must have worked from memory rather than using a traditional pattern. The bakery painting comes from a private house. One feels that it glorifies the owner's trade (or at least his business interests), which is made to look as genteel as possible. It has also been suggested that the central figure is an official, seeking popularity by the free distribution of bread.

Bianchi Bandinelli, illus. 50, fig. 50; Grant, *Cities of Vesuvius* 207.

228

229

230

229
Large hexagonal glass flagon
Height 35 cm
Naples Museum, inv. 13181
From Pompeii

The body was blown into a mold, and the rim turned out and polished. The large, flat handle with combed lines was welded on separately. Such bottles were used for storing liquids, and the form is also found in smaller, short versions.

230
Tall square glass bottle
Height 41 cm
Naples Museum, inv. 13009
From Pompeii

A taller version of No. 231, but blown into a mold. The type appears about the middle of the first century A.D. Such bottles were used all over the Empire for containing liquids, their shape making them very easy to pack. A wooden box of them was found in the House of the Menander.
Isings 66, form 50b; Maiuri, *Menandro* 457f.

231

233

232

234

231
Low square glass bottle
Height 21 cm
Naples Museum, inv. 114835
From Pompeii, atrium of IX, 8, 6

An unusually large version of an otherwise common form, free blown and squared off by pressure on a flat marble surface. It was found together with 3 similar bottles, 6 square storage jars, several cylindrical jars, and other flasks in a house that in the final period was used commercially, presumably by a dealer in whatever these receptacles contained.
Isings 63f., form 50a.

232
Triangular glass bottle
Height 16.5 cm
Naples Museum, inv. 13075
From Pompeii

One of a pair. Blown into a mold, the handle, a flattened bar of glass, welded on separately. The shape is unusual, as yet known only at Pompeii.
Isings 66.

233
Two glass bottles in a pottery basket
Height of bottles: 16 cm and 8.6 cm
Basket: height 14.5 cm, length 22.5 cm
Naples Museum, inv. 12845, 12895-6
From Pompeii

The two bottles are small, straight-sided versions of a common cylindrical storage jar, blown into a mold. The handles, made of thick flat bars of glass, are welded on separately.
MB 3 (Rome 1839) 240, pl. II.

234
Bronze steelyard balance
Height (from hook to plate) 73.5 cm, length of arm 31 cm
Naples Museum, inv. 74039
From Pompeii

The balance operates on the familiar principle of the steelyard, with an eccentric fulcrum, the scale pan hanging from the shorter arm and the counterweight hanging from a loop that is free to move along a graduated scale along the longer arm as described by Vitruvius (x, 3, 4). Commonly, as in this example, there are two alternative positions of the fulcrum and two corresponding graduated scales, one of which reads (in Roman numerals) from 1 to 14, the other from 10 to 50. The counterweight is in the form of the bust of a boy, perhaps the portrait of a young member of the Imperial family. The eyes are inlaid in silver.

An inscription punched in dots on the shorter arm gives the consular date A.D. 47 and certifies that the weights are in accordance with the specifications laid down in that year by the Roman aediles Marcus Articuleianus and Gnaeus Turranius and known as "the Articuleiana." Standard weights and measures were an important feature of the Roman commercial system, and in this case it was the official standards established in Rome that were the point of reference.

CIL X. 2, 8067.2; Daremberg and Saglio, s.v. *Libra*.

235
Bronze balance
Length of arm 26 cm, drop of scale-pans 29 cm
Naples Museum, inv. 116438
From the House of the Centenary (IX, 8, 3)

The scales are of the simple equipoise type, hung from a hook in the center of the arm. They were found in the southwest corner of the western atrium, along with various other balances, forceps, and pincers, together constituting what appears to be the equipment of a doctor. The cup-shaped pans would have been very suitable for weighing powders and other loose medical commodities.

236
Bronze stamp
Length 6.8 cm, width 2.3 cm
Pompeii, Antiquarium, inv. 1870-4
From the entrance to the Thermopolium (VI, 16, 33), 27 June 1904

The stamp gives, in abbreviated form, the name of Lucius Aurunculeius Secundio, a member of a family that came originally from Suessa (Sessa Aurunca), a town in northern Campania, 42 miles from Pompeii. Such stamps (*signacula*), bearing the name of the owner of a workshop or of his agent, were widely used as trademarks and for advertisement in the manufacture not only of bricks, pottery, and lamps, but also of more ephemeral products such as loaves of bread. Several carbonized loaves in the Naples Museum are stamped *[C]eleris Q. Grani Veri ser[vi]*, "[Made by] Celer, slave of Quintus Granius Verus."

NSc 1908, 292; Castrén 141; Mau-Kelsey 497f.

236

235

237

238

237
Wall painting: warships
60.5 cm by 61 cm
Naples Museum, inv. 8554
From the Temple of Isis (VIII, 8, 28)

On the upper part of the fresco is an illusionistic seascape with warships. These galleys illustrate the type of fast, light craft that made up the Roman navy following its founding by Augustus and formed a part of the fleet commanded by the elder Pliny at Misenum. A painted cornice separates the seascape from the lower part of the fresco with its arrangement of leaves and flowers painted in exuberant arabesques on a solid black background.

Mon. Pitt. III, fig. 8; cf. L. Casson, *Ships and Seamanship in the Ancient World* (Princeton 1971) 144, note 15.

238 (color plate, vol. I, p. 75)
Fish mosaic
Originally about 90 cm square
Naples Museum, inv. 120177
From House VIII, 2, 16

A studio piece made of very fine tesserae, laid within a tray-like frame of terracotta,

for use as the central panel (*emblema*) of a larger, less delicate pavement, the design of which is not known. It probably belonged initially to House VIII, 2, 14 and was reused when this was rebuilt in the early Empire and incorporated in this much larger House VIII, 2, 16.

Against a black background is displayed a gallery of edible sea creatures, portrayed with a lively naturalism that enables most of them to be identified, in almost all cases, with species still found and fished in the Bay of Naples. Among the more familiar are octopus, squid, lobster, prawn, eel, bass, red mullet, dogfish, ray, wrasse, and a murex shell. The inclusion in the left margin of a small stretch of rocky landscape, which is quite out of character, is perhaps to be explained as a fill-in taken from a different source. There are several other mosaics at Pompeii that are so similar in subject and workmanship that they must be derived from the same original and are very possibly by the same hand. About 100 B.C.

O. Keller, *Die antike Tierwelt* (Leipzig 1913) 393; Pernice VI, 151; A. Palombi, "La fauna marina nei mosaici e nei dipinti Pompeiani," *Pompeiana* (1950) 427-429.

239
Still life painting: loaf of bread and two figs
Width 23 cm, height 23 cm
Naples Museum, inv. 8625
From Herculaneum

Still lifes, rare in the Second and Third Styles, were very popular in the last period, when they were commonly used as parts of larger compositions.

The circular loaf, marked out into seven sections, closely resembles the surviving carbonized examples found at Pompeii and at Herculaneum. The figs are displayed on a window ledge, a favorite mannerism of these still lifes. This little panel probably comes from a Fourth Style architectural scheme.

Beyen, *Stilleben* 81, note 1; Croisille 33, no. 24.

240 (color plate, vol. I, p. 76)
Four still life panels
Width 1.54 m, height 37 cm
Naples Museum, inv. 8647
From Herculaneum

Each of these panels was originally the centerpiece of a large panel in a Fourth Style wall, as in the peristyle of the House of the Dioscuri. After being cut out,'they were framed together to form a frieze. The first two are very different in style from the other two.
a. A plucked chicken, hung by its feet, and a rabbit hung by one forepaw.
b. Left, strung from a ring by its beak, a partridge. Right, a pomegranate and an apple.
c. Upper shelf, three thrushes. Lower shelf, six pink mushrooms.
d. Upper shelf, two birds, probably partridges. Below, two eels.

Beyen, *Stilleben* 59ff.; Croisille 40, no. 46.

241 (color plate, vol. I, p. 74)
Two large painted panels with still lifes
Height 74 cm, width 2.34 m
Naples Museum, inv. 8611
From the *triclinium* on the west side of the garden, which lies within the property (*praedia*) of Julia Felix (II, 4, 3)

These two still lifes, which are unusually large, come from the upper part of the Fourth Style walls of a dining room.
a. (damaged). Lower step, part of a vase, with its lid leaning against it, a strip of woolen material, and a two-handled drinking cup (*kylix*). Upper step, a cockerel with its head dangling, dripping blood.
b. A raised block carrying a large glass bowl full of fruit (apples, pomegranates, grapes, figs). At a lower level, a pottery vase containing dried fruit (prunes?) and, leaning against it, a small amphora-shaped jar, its lid tightly sealed by means of cords attached to the handles.

Beyen, *Stilleben* 30, no. 2; Croisille 30, no. 11.

239

240
241

242

242 (color plate, vol. I, p. 76)
Three painted still life panels
Width 1.29 m, height 41 cm
Naples Museum, inv. 8644
From Herculaneum

Each of these panels was originally the centerpiece of a large panel in a Fourth Style wall (cf. No. 241). After being cut out they were framed together to form a frieze.
a. Young bird and a light-colored pottery jug, over the mouth of which is placed a glass beaker with rilled decoration of a type frequently found in Campania and possibly manufactured at Puteoli (Pozzuoli.) On the shelf above are indistinct objects: leaves, material, or possibly sheets of tripe.
b. Silver vase, with a small bird perched on its tall handle; a trident; seafood and shellfish (*frutta di mare*), including murex shells; and a large crayfish. On the shelf above, two cuttlefish.
c. A rabbit nibbling at a bunch of grapes and a dead partridge hanging from a ring. In the window, a large red apple.
Beyen, *Stilleben* 72ff.; Croisille 39f., no. 43.

243 (color plate, vol. I, p. 77)
Composite picture made up of four separate fragments taken from Fourth Style walls
Width 49 cm, height 43 cm
Naples Museum, inv. 9819
The writing materials and the still life came from Herculaneum, the other two from somewhere in the Vesuvius area.

a. A silver urn, probably from the upper zone of a wall.
b. Left, two book-scrolls of papyrus, one half-unrolled; the titles, on little tags, hang from the wooden baton on which the papyrus is rolled. Right, a diptych, or wooden two-leafed writing tablet (as No. 17).
c. Landscape: a rustic shrine with figures.
d. Half of a still life panel, similar to Nos. 240-242: an apple, a pear, and a pomegranate.
Croisille 52.

244, 245
Wall paintings: scenes of banqueting
Naples Museum, inv. 120029, 120031
From House V, 2, 4

Two of three related panels that consti-

tuted the centers of the Fourth Style compositions in the *triclinium* at the northwest corner of the peristyle. All three portray the three couches appropriate to a *triclinium,* but the actual ⊓ -shaped arrangement is opened out to simplify the composition. Though often interpreted as showing the successive stages of a single feast, the fact that the secondary figures of the side panels of the same walls illustrated personifications of the Seasons suggests rather that they are views of separate banquets held on various occasions. The third scene (inv. 120030), which included musicians and nude dancing girls, is unfortunately not well preserved.

244
Width 66 cm, height 68 cm

On the left-hand couch a reclining man places his hand on the shoulder of a second man, perhaps a late arrival, also seated, having his shoes removed while a slave offers him a cup. Faintly legible above the figures are the letters SCIO ("I know"). On the middle couch one man lies back raising a large cup while another is helped into his cloak by a slave; above the first man, BIBO ("I drink"). The right-hand couch is empty, and beside it a man, supported by a youth, leans over, apparently vomiting.

245
Width 60 cm, height 64 cm

Apparently a summer banquet, held in a garden under an awning. In the middle is a table set for food and drink and a young slave brings wine in a pair of *askoi.* On the left-hand couch reclines a couple, nude from the waist up; the woman raises a drinking horn *(rhyton)* to her mouth, while her companion holds a plate *(patera).* A single figure on the central couch, the host, addresses the company with the words: FACITIS. VOBIS. SVAVITER. EGO. CANTO. ("Enjoy yourselves. I'm singing.") Of the couple on the right-hand couch, the man holds a drinking cup *(cantharus)* and replies: EST. ITA. VALEAS. ("OK. Good luck to you.")
Mau, *Bull Inst.* LVII (1885), 254f., nos. 13 and 12; Schefold, *WP* 71.

246
Wall painting: woman surprising two lovers
Width 52 cm, height 60 cm
Naples Museum, inv. 111209
From a room beside the *fauces* of House VI, 14, 29

The scene, of which several other versions are known, comes from a late Fourth Style wall. Its exact significance is unknown. A man and woman recline on a couch, eating bread and fruit from a table; she holds a silver drinking cup *(cantharus).* They are looking, in apparent surprise, toward another woman who enters from the left followed by a small attendant carrying a casket.
Sogliano 641.

247 (color plate, vol. I, p. 66)
Wall painting: entertainment after a meal
Width 46 cm, height 44 cm
Naples Museum, inv. 9016
From House I, 3, 18 at Pompeii

The central panel picture (now rather faded) of a Third Style wall. The diners recline on couches, the empty dishes and cups piled on the table and floor. In the center a girl who has picked up a silver ladle is dancing to the tune of the double pipes, watched by the woman seated on the left. On the right, another seated woman, heavily draped, is perhaps a chaperone, and peeping round the curtain are two small attendants.

Such scenes are frequently found on Pompeian walls (see No. 246); they derive from Hellenistic originals of which the exact meaning is now lost.
Schefold, *WP* 12 and 334.

248
Large bronze two-handled bowl
Diameter 34.5 cm, height 12.2 cm
Naples Museum, inv. 73599
From Pompeii

The two handles consist of a series of ring moldings grasped in the mouth of a pair of dolphins, which spring outward from a Silenus head escutcheon on the underside of the rim.
Pernice IV, 10ff.

243

248

244

245

246

247

249 250

249
Bronze jug with long spout
Height 16 cm
Naples Museum, inv. 69148
From Pompeii

Globular jug with a long channeled spout. The handle, which is decorated with two swans in low relief, ends in a Medusa head.

250
Bronze jug (oenochoe)
Height 13 cm
Naples Museum, inv. 69018
From Herculaneum

Apart from shallow grooves at the base of the neck, the rounded body is plain. The mouth is pinched in to form a deeply lobed spout. The ornament is concentrated on the elegant, upstanding handle, which was cast separately: at the top, facing forward, a lion's head, and at the junction with the body, in place of the animal's paw that is usually found in combination with the lion's head, a boss in the form of a woman's head in an Egyptian headdress. Similar pieces found in central Europe (e.g., A. Radnoti, *Die römischen Bronzegefässe von Pannonien* [Budapest 1938] pls. XIII, 72, and XLIX, I) are either actual exports from Campania or are local pieces influenced by such exports.
Cf. *MB* 3 (Rome 1839) pls. XXVII; Pernice, *AA* 1900, 187, no. 14.

251

251
Bronze jug (oenochoe)
Height 20 cm
Naples Museum, inv. 69046
From one of the sites in the Vesuvius area

The elegant vertical channeling was engraved after casting. An escutcheon in the form of a siren perched on a foliated boss marks the point of junction of the ribbed handle with the body.

252
Bronze jar (amphorula)
Height 39.5 cm
Naples Museum, inv. 69629
From one of the sites in the Vesuvius area

There are two identical examples of this type of jar in the Naples Museum. The handles are made in the form of two ribbed plant stems with leaves at the lower ends, joined with volutes to an escutcheon in the form of the figure of a swan with a snake in its mouth.

252

253
Bronze strainer
Length 32 cm, diameter of bowl 11 cm, height 7.5 cm
Naples Museum, inv. 77605
From Pompeii

The simple but decoratively detailed bronze strainer was probably used for straining wine. Perforations form a rosette in the bottom of the bowl, encircled by a wavy band between straight lines, and, on the side, a meander. A long flat handle with a crisply contoured profile extends

253

from the out-turned lip, and on the handle is the inscription *Victor fe[cit],* "Victor made it." The simple formula suggests that Victor was a slave or freedman, belonging to a generation of enterprising workmen who transplanted workshops from Italy (Campania?) to Gaul.
Spinazzola 300 (upper right); Chiurazzi 180, no. 356; A. Carandini, "Alcune forme bronzee conservate a Pompei e nel Museo Nazionale di Napoli," in *L' instrumentum domesticum di Ercolano e Pompei* (Rome 1977) 167.

254
Bronze handle from a vessel
Length 17.3 cm
Naples Museum, inv. 72663
From one of the sites in the Vesuvius area

One of a pair of cast bronze handles, probably from an amphorula of the same shape as No. 252. Along the handle, in low relief, is a plant design incorporating acanthus leaves, and on the escutcheon, where it was soldered to the body of the vessel, a bearded male head with wild hair and pointed ears, either Pan or a satyr. The eyes are inlaid in silver.
Cf. Pernice, *AA* 1900, 184, nos. 9 and 10; Tassinari, *Gallia* Suppl. 29 (Paris 1975) no. 187.

254

255

255
Curved bronze handle decorated with amorino and sea horses
Length 13 cm
Naples Museum, inv. 72972
From Herculaneum

A little winged amorino is perched on the curling tails of two sea horses; below them are gently rolling waves. The group originally formed a handle, possibly one of a pair, on the edge of a large flat plate.
MB 9 (Rome 1845) 232, pl. L; *Bronzi di Ercolano* I, 25 and 275, note 15.

256, 257
Pair of handles in the form of human hands
Bronze
Overall width 18 cm
Naples Museum, inv. 123300, 76/118
From Pompeii

The hands are linked by a channeled grip, decorated at the midpoint with a ring set with small knobs. Along the base of each hand is a flat strip that ends in two bird's-head volutes. Such handles, sometimes with smooth grips and rosettes on the rings in place of the little knobs, are found on large bowls and, on a much larger scale, on stoves and equipment for heating liquids.

Pernice IV, 31f.; H. Willers, *Neue Untersuchungen über die römische Bronzeindustrie von Capua und von Niedergermanien* (Hannover and Leipzig 1907) 72.

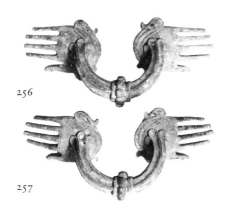

256

257

258

259

258
Red pottery (terra sigillata) plate
Height 4.3 cm, diameter 17.6 cm
Pompeii, Storerooms, inv. 13168

Plates of this kind are found in great quantity at Pompeii and must have been part of the standard, better-quality earthenware table setting. The vertical rim forms a background for a decoration of thunderbolts and rosettes, which were made separately of clay and applied before the plate was given its coating of highly purified clay slip and fired. A footprint-shaped

260-262

stamp contains the initials G N. AT. A[.], used by one of the potters trained in Arezzo who set up workshops in Pozzuoli (Puteoli) on the Bay of Naples.

C. Goudineau, *La céramique arétine lisse* (Paris 1968) 306, type 39; A Oxé and H. Comfort, *Corpus vasorum arretinorum* (Bonn 1968) nos. 146, 147 or 149; G. Pucci, "Le sigillate italiche, galliche e orientali" in *L' instrumentum domesticum di Ercolano e Pompei* (Rome 1977) 14.

259
Red pottery (terra sigillata) bowl
Height 6.8 cm, diameter 12.3 cm
Pompeii, Antiquarium, inv. 408-3

The vertical rim has an applied decoration of rabbits and rosettes and helmet-like forms. This kind of appliqué ornament was easily executed and apparently inexpensive since it enjoyed great popularity in the first century. The bowl carries the stamp of L. Rasinius Pisanus, a potter who worked at a still unlocated site in Italy.

C. Goudineau, *La céramique arétine lisse* (Paris 1968) 305, type 38; A. Oxé and H. Comfort, *Corpus vasorum arretinorum* (Bonn 1968) no. 1558, 93, 94; G. Pucci, "Le sigillate italiche, galliche e orientali" in *L' instrumentum domesticum di Ercolano e Pompei* (Rome 1977) 13.

260–262 (color plate, vol. I, p. 29)
Three red pottery (terra sigillata) bowls
Found in the *tablinum* of House VIII, 5, 9 on 4 October 1881, together with eighty-seven others of the same forms and thirty-seven pottery lamps, all packed in a wooden crate. The bowls were made by several different Gaulish potters, and the lamps were probably made in northern Italy. This suggests that the Pompeian consignee had dealt through an agent in the north rather than directly with the potteries.

260
Diameter 20.5 cm
Naples Museum, inv. 112974

Stamped in the center of the inside by the maker Vitalis, who was active about A.D. 60-85. There were five of his bowls in the consignment, all of the same form (Dragendorf 29). The decoration comprises an upper frieze of festoons enclosing large rosettes, and a lower one of trellised zigzag lines with one or two little rosettes in the spaces.

D. Atkinson, *JRS* 4 (1914) 49, no. 28.

261
Diameter 16 cm
Naples Museum, inv. 112984

Stamped as No. 260 but by Mommo, one of the most prolific of South Gaulish potters. Twenty-three of his bowls of this form (Dragendorf 29) and ten more of the same shape as No. 262 (Dragendorf 37) were found in the crate. The two bands of decoration are divided into rectangular panels, the upper containing arrowhead shapes alternating with running dogs, the lower, amorini and stylized flowers.

D. Atkinson, *JRS* 4 (1914) 44, no. 8.

262
Diameter 16.8 cm
Naples Museum, inv. 112997

The letters MOM were incised in the mold in large cursive letters under the decoration, probably by the potter Mommo (see No. 261). The form is Dragendorf 37, one of the commonest of the Gaulish forms. Below a band of ovolo moldings and a wreath of ivy leaves is a broader zone of rectangular panels containing alternately S-shaped patterns above circles and pairs of human figures. Round the bottom runs a chain of V-shaped leaves.

D. Atkinson, *JRS* 4 (1914) 56, no. 54.

263

263

Red-orange pottery amphorula
Height 21.5 cm
Naples Museum, inv. 110388
From Pompeii

The jar copies the form of bronze vessels like No. 252. The glossy surface is created by coating the piece with a highly purified version of the body clay. This jar was made in the area of modern Tunisia, where the foundations of an enormously successful export business were being laid.

J. W. Hayes, *Late Roman Pottery* (London 1972) 190, form 161, 1.

264

Carpenter's plane of iron
Length 19 cm, height 10 cm
Naples Museum, inv. 71964
From Pompeii

The tool bears a close resemblance to the traditional carpenter's plane except that the stock was made of iron, possibly with a wooden handle. The angle of the share, or cutting edge, seems to have been adjustable.

265

Iron hammer
Length 26 cm
Naples Museum, inv. 71883
From Pompeii

As in a modern geologist's hammer, the handle is made in one piece with the head. Ordinary carpenter's hammer-heads, socketed for wooden handles, have also been found at Pompeii, which suggests that this piece may be a specialized tool used by some other type of craftsman.

266

Bronze folding rule
Length 29 cm
Naples Museum, inv. 76696
From Pompeii

The rule is divided into two equal parts, hinged at the center. One half carries a small bar on one side, pivoted so as to slot into two hooks on the other half and hold the fully extended rule rigid. Although the length falls just short of a standard Roman foot (about 29.45 cm), this lies well within the margin of error permissible in a system that for most practical purposes depended more on relative proportions than on absolute dimensions.

267

Bronze plumb-bob
Diameter 5.6 cm, height 4.5 cm
Naples Museum, inv. 76661
From Pompeii

A solid inverted cone of very slightly concave profile, with a small knob in the middle of the top to take the string and another at the point.

268

Broad mason's chisel of iron
Length 19 cm, width of blade 9 cm
Naples Museum, inv. 71771
From Pompeii

Although of little use on hard stone, a chisel of this sort would have been very effective on the softer local volcanic tufa, both for splitting and for squaring off the faces.

269

Bronze compass
Length of arm 20 cm
Naples Museum, inv. 76686

The form is indistinguishable from the simpler types in modern use.

270

Bronze callipers
Length 15 cm
Naples Museum, inv. 76/266
From one of the sites in the Vesuvius area

The form, hinged at the top with two inward-curving arms, is indistinguishable from that in use today.

271

Bronze carpenter's or mason's square
16.1 by 16.1 cm
Naples Museum, inv. 78/321

The tool differs from most modern squares in having a flange on one of the outer edges. This feature was probably intended to render the square more stable. The ends have an ornamental profile.

264

265

266

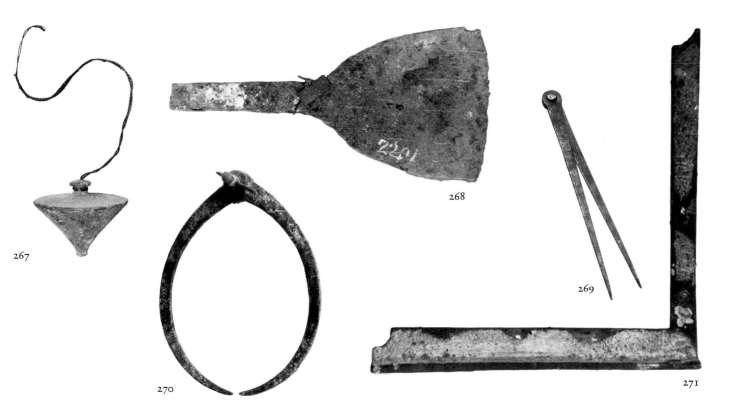

267

268

269

270

271

272
Bronze pen
Length 12.9 cm
Naples Museum, inv. 78/279

Pens were usually fashioned of hollow reeds, with one end sharpened to a point (see No. 274). For a pen of bronze or copper, a thin sheet of metal was rolled to approximate the shape of the hollow reed, with one end of the metal worked into a point.

273
Bronze inkwell
Height 5 cm
Naples Museum, inv. 75083

The inkwell is in the form of a cylinder made from a rolled strip of bronze with discs applied to top and bottom ends. A highly stylized ivy vine is incised around the opening. The lid with its off-center grip turns on a carefully made hinge.

274
Wall painting: writing instruments
Width 41 cm, height 16.8 cm
Naples Museum, inv. 4676
From Pompeii

Wax tablets, a double inkwell and a papyrus or parchment scroll, with a reed pen and a small bag for carrying sharp-pointed pens and *styli*, make up a group of typical Pompeian writing implements (see No. 17).

A wax tablet, *tabula cerata*, was a flat, rectangular wood or metal tablet with raised edges, upon which a thin layer of wax was spread. The writing was scratched into the surface of the wax with a *stylus*, a slender shaft of brass-covered iron or bone, with a sharp point at one end and flattened at the other for smoothing the wax so that it could be reused. Several tablets might be joined by small cords to form a kind of book, with each tablet having a small wooden button at the center to separate the surfaces of adjoining tablets and protect the writing. Such tablets were used for notes and

memoranda, letters, accounts, and children's lessons at school.

More permanent records and works of literary worth were written in ink on a *volumen*, or scroll, using a sharpened quill or reed pen, or, more rarely, a copper or bronze pen (see No. 272). The writer or reader would unroll the scroll to reveal one section at a time. The section of scroll pictured in the fresco is only partially completed, and the writer has rested his pen for a while against the inkwell. The open chamber of the well probably held black ink, made of soot, cuttlefish ink, wine dregs, and water. The other chamber may have held red ink, made from cinnabar.

T. Dyer, *Pompeii* (London 1871) 534; Croisille pls. CIX, 205, CX, 207.

272,273

274

275
Inscribed slab recording the architect of the theater
Marble, restored from 3 pieces
Length 90.5 cm, height 23 cm
Naples Museum, inv. 3834
Found in 1792 in the Large Theater

275

M[arcus] Artorius M[arci]
l[ibertus] Primus architectus.
"Marcus Artorius Primus, freedman of
Marcus [Artorius, was] the architect."

The inscription relates to the major
reconstruction of the Theater undertaken
during the reign of Augustus. The work
on the seating area and its substructures is
known to have been undertaken by the
Holconius brothers (see pages 39f.) around
the turn of the first centuries B.C. and A.D.
(*CIL* x. 833, 834). The even more radical
reconstruction of the stage building (to
which this inscription may refer) was evidently financed separately but was roughly
contemporary.

The architect was a freedman of the
Artorii, a local Campanian family, and
may well have learned his profession as a
slave, working with another architect. His
name appears also on a fragmentary
marble epistyle (*CIL* x. 807) found, dis-
placed, to the west of the Temple of Venus
and attributed by Fiorelli to the columnar
structure (*tribunal*) at the west end of the
Basilica.
CIL x. 841; *ILS* 5638a; Castrén no. 44, 4.

276
Relief showing a coppersmith's workshop
Italian marble
Height 42 cm, width 54 cm
Naples Museum, inv. 6575
From Pompeii

The relief was probably set into the wall
of a workshop. It illustrates three of the
main processes of the coppersmith's craft.
In the center the smith is seated on a
bench, holding with a pair of tongs a lump
of hot metal on a small anvil, ready to be
struck by an assistant who wields a heavy
hammer; above are the heavy double
doors of the furnace. On the right the
smith is seated at a bench, engraving or
embossing a large circular dish. Above
him crouches an animal (a watch-dog?),
and above that is an assortment of pastry-
molds, dishes, plates, and buckets. On the
left, he is weighing something out in a
large pair of scales. Although there must
have been a special charge for his more
elaborate pieces, it is likely that, as in
many early societies, the simpler pieces
were sold by weight.
O. Jahn, *Berichten der phil.-hist. Classe der*
Königl. Sächs. Gesellschaft der Wissenschaf-
ten 1861, 360ff.; H. Blümner, *Technologie und*
Terminologie der Gewerbe und Künste IV
(Leipzig 1884) 251.

277-280
In classical times the normal bulk container was the amphora, a vessel with a
large pointed or rounded body and a very
strong neck with two handles. The great
majority of these were used for wine and
oil, but they could also be put to more
specialized uses, e.g., in Campania for soft
fruits and for the fermented fish-paste,
garum, a delicacy known to have been
produced at Pompeii. There is no direct
relationship between the shapes and their
contents, and they were commonly reused
for products quite different from those for
which they were originally manufactured.
The producing areas normally established
potteries of their own, and the characteristic shapes and fabrics are an invaluable
index of the patterns of commerce.

277
Large wine amphora
Height 1.21 m
Pompeii, Storerooms, inv. 15391

Amphoras of this form (Dressel IB) were
made in Italy during the second and first
centuries B.C., especially in northern Campania, where they were used to contain
Falernian and Caecuban wines. These
wines were highly esteemed in their day
and are known to have been aged in the
amphora. The inside would have been
given a coating of pitch to seal the otherwise porous fabric, and the mouth was
stopped with a cork disc fixed with
pozzolana cement.

278
Wide-mouthed amphora (Dressel form 22)
Height 87 cm
Pompeii, Storerooms, inv. 15450

The painted inscription on the neck reads
MAL[a] CVM[ana] VER[a] ("Real
Cumaean fruits") followed by the weight
of the contents, *LXIIII* (64 pounds) and
the letters *P.C.Z,* presumably the initials
of the owner or consignee. Over the tail
of the *Z* is written the name of the agent
or bailiff who packed the amphora,
Cornelius[?].

279
Small amphora
Height 57 cm
Pompeii, Storerooms, inv. 15390

Small amphoras of this type are hardly
ever found in the commercial cargoes re-
covered from shipwrecks. It was produced
for local purposes within the Pompeian
area.

280
Cylindrical amphora
Height 88 cm
Pompeii, Storerooms, inv. 15451
From a room in the garden of the House
of the Centenary (IX, 8, 6)

Recent studies have shown that there are
many varieties of cylindrical amphoras of
this general form, classified by Schoene
(*CIL* IV) as form 11. This particular example falls within the range of Ostia form
LIX (Panella 571-572, 632, nos. 48, 49).
They were probably made in North Africa
and contained olive oil (cf. Beltram Lloris
522-523). The mouth would have been
sealed with a terracotta disc fixed in position with wax.

On the neck is painted the name *L[uci]*
Helvi Zos[imi], possibly that of the agent
or shipper.
CIL IV, Supp. 5847.

281
Wall painting of a potter at his wheel
Height 75 cm, width 54 cm
Pompeii, Antiquarium, inv. 2193-4
From a potter's workshop (II, 3, 7) on the
outside of the southwest corner of the
shop

The potter is shown seated on a low
wooden stool, dressed in the customary
short workman's tunic and working at a
tall jug mounted on a simple kick wheel.
Beside him on the ground are several
small jugs and vases. To the left stands the
figure of Vulcan, Roman god of fire,
protector of furnaces and kilns.

Most of the ordinary pottery in domestic use at Pompeii (see Nos. 282-287)
was made locally. Several potters' workshops are attested, including a large one
outside the Herculaneum Gate (Mau-
Kelsey 378) and one, which also made
amphoras, in I, 20, 2-3.
NSc 1939, 198ff.

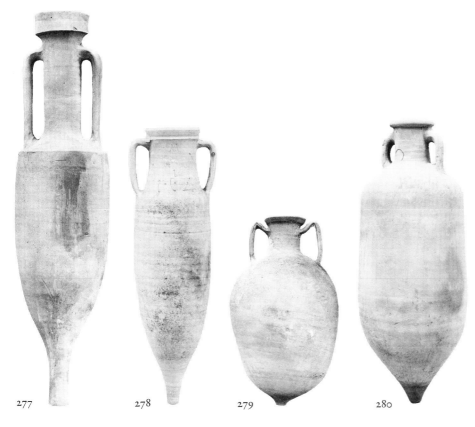

277   278   279   280

282
Large, squat one-handled jug
Height 14 cm, diameter 26 cm
Pompeii, Storerooms, inv. 15397

Made in thick, coarse pottery, the jug was probably used for water, the thick walls and small mouth helping to keep it cool in hot weather.

283
Pottery jug with trefoil lip
Height 23 cm
Pompeii, Storerooms, inv. 15396

Rather finer ware than the other local domestic pottery exhibited, it was probably used for serving wine or water in a bar or tavern, or in one of the poorer private houses. The form is derived from the Greek *oenochoe*.

284
Cooking pot on a pottery stand
Height of pot 28 cm, height of stand 16 cm
Pompeii, Storerooms, inv. 15398, 15399, 15395

A slightly larger version of No. 286. Because the underside was rounded, such pots needed a stand for serving or for storage.

285
Pottery strainer
Height 23.5 cm, diameter 26 cm
Pompeii, Storerooms, inv. 15393

The rounded bottom of the vessel is perforated by a series of holes, of the size of knitting needles; the handles are designed for suspension, and the grooved neck would have been suitable for tying a cloth over the mouth. A number of vessels of this specialized form have been found. They may well have been used for straining curd cheese to make ricotta, which was a major component of Roman cookery, just as today it is still very widely used in the preparation of typical south Italian dishes.

276

281

282   283   284   285   286   287

286
Cooking pot on an iron stand
Height of pot 26 cm, greatest diameter
24 cm
Pompeii, Storerooms, inv. 15394, 15394b

Jars of this distinctive form, with or
without handles and found in varying
sizes (see No. 284), were regularly used
for cooking, placed directly on an open
charcoal fire or else, as in this instance, on
an iron support.

287
Pottery bowl
Height 13.5 cm, diameter 27 cm
Pompeii, Storerooms, inv. 15392

Hundreds of these general-purpose
kitchen bowls, of varying sizes, have been
found in Pompeian houses. They were
used for the storage, preparation, and
serving of food.

287a
Terracotta cooking pan with lid
Pan: height 5.9 cm, diameter 21.6 cm
Lid: height 5.7 cm, diameter 21.8 cm
Pompeii, Storerooms, inv. 665

This kind of pan could be used either for
cooking or for serving. The gray bands on
the exterior are the result of uneven firing
conditions. Imported pans were in use in
many Roman cities, but in Pompeii local
potters managed to hold off the out-of-
town competition.

287a

VII Leisure

288, 289
Two terracotta figurines of gladiators
Height 13 cm
Naples Museum, inv. 20340, 20259
From Pompeii

Probably from the same mold, one of
them (20340) preserving traces of coloring. The figure wears greaves (*ocreae*; see
No. 295) on both legs, an unvisored helmet with a crest and a breech cloth, and
his exposed right arm is bound with
leather thongs; he carries a strongly convex shield *(parma)* and is armed with a
short sword. His costume and armor are
those of a "Thracian" *(Thrax)* except
that Thracian armor normally included a
very distinctive, sickle-shaped scimitar.
The *Thrax* was usually matched against
a heavily armed *Hoplomachus,* or "Samnite," or the lighter *Myrmillo.* It seems
likely that such figurines of gladiators
(see also Nos. 290, 291) served as small
gifts presented on the occasion of the New
Year feast of the Saturnalia.
Von Rohden 52 and pl. 41, 1; Levi nos. 851,
852; Winter II, 387, 2b and 2c.

290
Terracotta figurine of a gladiator
Height 12 cm
Naples Museum, inv. 20260

The figure wears a single greave on the
left leg and a visored helmet with a tall,
angular crest. He carries a large, rectangular, curved shield and is armed with a
short sword. His armor and weapon indicate that he is one of a rather ill-defined
group of heavily armed gladiators, all of
whom seem to be variants of the original
Hoplomachus, or "Samnite" type.
Von Rohden pl. 41, 1; Levi no. 851; Winter II,
387, 2d.

291
Terracotta figurine of a gladiator
Height 14 cm
Naples Museum, inv. 20341
From the House of Marcus Lucretius
(IX, 3, 5)

Like Nos. 288, 289, he wears two greaves
and a crested helmet; but the helmet is
visored, his shield, though small, is rectangular, and he wears a tunic. His weapon is missing. Perhaps a variant of the
Thrax.
Von Rohden 52; Levi no. 852; Winter II,
387, 2c.

292
Bronze gladiator's helmet
Height 40 cm, width across neck guard
33 cm
Naples Museum, inv. 5643
From Herculaneum

A heavily armored gladiator's fighting
helmet, without decoration. The visor,
which includes a broad flange pierced with
two holes to fasten it down, is made in
four parts, riveted together and strengthened by a strip of bronze running from the
brow to the chin. It is hinged to the helmet
behind the ears. A broader flange around
the base of the helmet itself protected the
back of the neck and part of the shoulders.
Fiorelli, *Armi antiche* no. 273.

293
Bronze gladiator's helmet
Height 45.5 cm, length 41 cm
Naples Museum, inv. 5650
From Pompeii

This type of bronze gladiatorial helmet
was a part of the full-dress armor of a
"Samnite" gladiator. The casque is decorated with the head of a sea-nymph rising from the waves at the center, flanked
on either side by a snail shell *(turritella)*
and a leaping dolphin. The high crest
ends in a griffin's head. To protect the
face, the helmet is fitted with two half-
visors, each formed of a network of bronze
rings with a solid flanged section below.
A strip of bronze as reinforcement runs
from top to bottom between the two sections. The initials *M C P* are incised in
the brim.

294
Gladiator's bronze shoulder armor
Length 30.5 cm, height 30.5 cm
Naples Museum, inv. 5639
From Pompeii

Shoulder armor was part of the equipment of a *retiarius,* whose weapons were
a net, trident, and dagger. Appropriately,
this "net-man" chose to have his armor
decorated with marine emblems such as
a crab, an anchor, a rudder, and a dolphin
twisting around a trident.

295
Pair of gladiator's bronze greaves
Length 53 cm, width 19.5 cm (both pieces)
Naples Museum, inv. 5666, 5667
From Pompeii

The rich relief decoration of this pair of
greaves, or leg protectors, is divided into
four zones containing Dionysiac symbols.

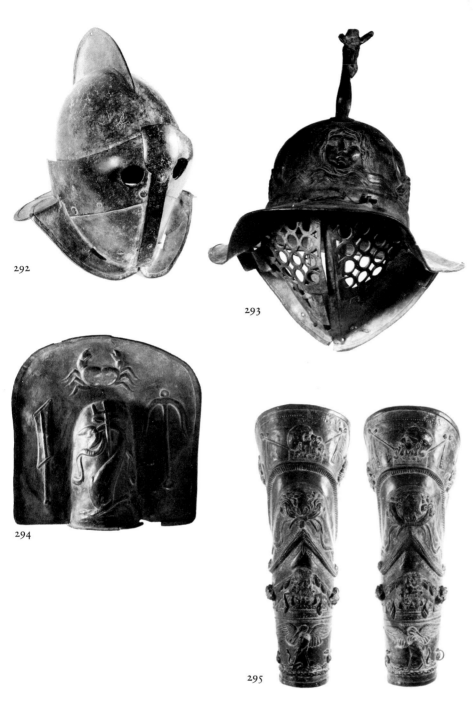

292

293

294

295

At the center of the top zone is the head of a Silenus between two *thyrsi,* with Bacchic masks on the sides, all resting in baskets. The zone covering the knee shows two horns of plenty, filled with fruit and spikes of grain tied with long fillets. Below this, on a lion's skin are three more Dionysiac masks, while, at the bottom, a stork with outspread wings attacks a serpent, which she will feed to her two little ones standing on the sides. Near the upper edge of both greaves are inscribed the letters *M C P.*

Chiurazzi 253, no. 582.

296
Gladiator's bronze shield
Diameter 37 cm
Naples Museum, inv. 5669
From Pompeii

The central silver boss, with a Medusa head in high relief, is surrounded by two concentric olive garlands in low relief and an outer border of olives and single olive leaves. This would have been a dress parade piece, although in shape and size it resembles the actual shields carried by some of the "Thracian" gladiators *(Thraeces)* and also by the mounted gladiators shown in the stucco reliefs on the Tomb of Umbricius Scaurus at Pompeii, now destroyed but known from drawings.

Fiorelli, *Armi antiche* no. 288.

297
Dagger
Iron, bone, and ivory
Length 30.5 cm, length of blade 19.4 cm
Naples Museum, inv. 5682
From Pompeii

A fighting weapon, with an iron blade of which the tang runs the full length of the grip, which is of bone with a pommel and guard of ivory. Such weapons were carried by the more lightly armed types of gladiator, including the *retiarii* (net-men), and by the *myrmillones.*

Fiorelli, *Armi antiche* no. 313.

288   289   290   291

296

297

303

303

Terracotta mask
Height 14 cm
Naples Museum, inv. 116712
Found in the atrium of House no. 24 on
the Via Stabiana, 7 August 1867

Replica of a theatrical mask, provided
with two small holes at the top for suspension. It is suggested that the furrowed
brow, hooked nose, and enormous open
mouth portray Maccus, the stock figure in
Atellan farce (see page 91), whose leading
characteristic seems to have been excess
of every sort.
Levi no. 874.

304

Amber statuette of an actor
Height 8.4 cm
Naples Museum, inv. 25813
From Pompeii

Probably a character from Roman mime,
wearing an ample cloak, the figure belongs
to a series of amber carvings on the same
theme of which Naples Museum has two
others and the British Museum five, said
to be from Nola. They were produced in
Aquileia, in northern Italy, about the
middle of the first century A.D. Amber was
highly prized by the Romans from the
early first century A.D. (when the trade
routes to the source of supplies in the Baltic
began to operate) as an amulet and for its
alleged medicinal qualities as well as for
carving. Roman women often carried a
piece in their hands in summer, and amber
carvings of animals, fruit, and ears of
wheat were given as New Year's presents.
Fiorelli, *Scavi* 157, no. 56 (20 Feb. 1863);
Siviero no. 568; D. E. Strong, *Catalogue of
the Carved Amber in the Department of
Greek and Roman Antiquities* (British Museum 1966) 5, 35, 91 and nos. 109-113.

304

305 (color plate, vol. I, p. 80)
Mosaic panel: rehearsing for a Satyr Play
Width 55 cm, height 54 cm
Naples Museum, inv. 9986
From the *tablinum* of the House of the
Tragic Poet (VI, 8, 5)

The rehearsal for a Greek Satyr Play, the
characteristic postlude for a Greek dramatic trilogy. The action takes place in
front of an Ionic portico hung with *oscilla*
(see No. 69) and draped with wreaths and
fillets, above which is an attic façade
decorated with pilasters, four large golden
wine vessels, and a pair of herm-like musicians. The bald and bearded figure wearing a Greek mantle (*himation*) and sandals
is the chorus master, possibly the drama-
tist himself. He watches two actors wearing goatskin loincloths, who appear to be
rehearsing dance steps to the notes of the
double pipes played by a richly robed and
garlanded musician (who would himself
have appeared on the stage). On the right
an attendant is helping another actor into
a shaggy Silenus costume. Behind the
seated figure, on a pedestal, is a male
tragic mask, and at his feet a female tragic
mask and a Silenus mask.

305

The mosaic, which was the centerpiece
of a black and white mosaic pavement
decorated with a meander pattern, is a
studio piece (*emblema*) derived from a
Hellenistic panel painting, perhaps one
painted to commemorate a victory in a
theatrical contest. In the course of adaptation to its present form the perspective of
the architectural setting has become hope-
lessly confused, with the two flanking
pilasters brought forward to consitute a
frame. It dates from the years between
A.D. 62 and 79.
E. Pfuhl, *Malerei und Zeichnung der Griechen*
(Munich 1923) 841f.; Pernice VI, 99f., 171;
Bieber, *Theater* 11f., 20, 130; Kraus and von
Matt no. 49.

306-309
Wall paintings: four theatrical masks

From the House of the Stags at Herculaneum, where they constituted the lower
parts of four of the vertical members that
divided the middle zone of the Fourth
Style scheme into panels. Each is shown
placed at the head of the steps leading up
onto a stage, within a frame of garlands
with Dionysiac attributes.

306
Mask of a father, in New Comedy
Length 97 cm, height 65 cm
Naples Museum, inv. 9838

The rolled arrangement of the hair, the
speira, was characteristic of New Comedy.
The white hair and beard indicate the role
of an old father.

307
Tragic mask of Andromeda
Length 93 cm, height 64 cm
Naples Museum, inv. 9850

Andromeda's mother, Cassiope, claimed
that her daughter was more beautiful than
the Nereids, and in expiation of this rash
boast Andromeda herself was exposed,
chained to a rock, to be devoured by a sea
monster sent by Poseidon. Perseus, using
the Gorgon's head to turn the monster
to stone, rescued and subsequently married her. See also the picture of this scene
in the House of the Priest Amandus (page
103).

308
Mask of a youth, in New Comedy
Length 66 cm, height 42 cm
Naples Museum, inv. 9804

The same hairstyle as No. 306. Beside the
mask is a book basket (*capsa*) and, on the
step, a short, curved staff (*pedum*).

309 (color plate, vol. I, p. 78)
Tragic mask of a youth
Length 62 cm, height 62 cm
Naples Museum, inv. 9805

His hair is piled high on his head and
crowned with a ribbon and a wreath of ivy
leaves. Against the steps leans a *thyrsus*.
Bieber, *Theater* 228; Agnes Allroggen-Bedel,
*Maskendarstellungen in der römisch-
kampanischen Wandmalerei* (Munich 1974)
126-127, nos. 2 (318), 6 (316), 4 (315), and
3 (317).

310

310
Wall painting of a scene from New Comedy

Height 29 cm, width 38 cm
Naples Museum, inv. 9034
From Stabiae

The panel, which was set into a larger wall scheme, is almost certainly a *pinax,* or painted replica of a late classical or early Hellenistic Greek panel picture. It portrays the dance group that in New Comedy took the place of the chorus in Old Comedy, consisting in this instance of a dwarf, a woman playing a double flute, and two men dancing, one of whom holds cymbals while the other beats a tambourine. The same Greek original is copied in a fine mosaic panel, signed by Dioscurides of Samos and datable to the end of the second century B.C., found in the so-called Villa of Cicero at Pompeii (Naples Museum, inv. 9985).

Bieber, *Theater* 95f.; Webster, *New Comedy* 192, NP 54.

311
Wall painting: erotic scene

Height 54 cm, width 51 cm
Naples Museum, inv. 27696
From Pompeii

The encounter takes place on a richly draped couch against a curtained background. The gestures come as much from the pornographic theater as from the world of sensuous pleasure. The painter was an inferior mannerist, relying on awkward rhetoric rather than suave anatomical understanding.

Grant, De Simone, and Merella 154, illus.

312
Wall painting: erotic scene

Height 37 cm, width 37 cm
Naples Museum, inv. 27697
From Pompeii

As is usual in Pompeian paintings with erotic subjects, the richness of the couch and draperies matches or, indeed, overshadows the action represented. The wreaths on the heads of the participants suggest these amorous frolics occurred after a symposium or banquet. Although erotic subjects played a small, private part in the art and life of Pompeii, scenes such as this have done much to influence the modern image of Roman decadence in the Julio-Claudian period of the Empire.

Grant, De Simone, and Merella 153, illus.

311

312

306

307

308

309

313

Little silver dish on a silver stand

Height together 5.5 cm, diameter of dish
8.6 cm, diameter of stand 7.9 cm
Naples Museum, inv. 25324 (dish) and
25547 (stand)
From Pompeii

The little tripod stand has animal's-paw
feet, and the edge is decorated with an
ovolo molding with traces of gilding. The
dish has thin crescent-shaped handles
decorated with elongated birds' heads and
rosettes (as on Nos. 320, 323).
Strong 153; cf. Maiuri, *Menandro* 364,
nos. 44-55.

314

Little silver dish on a silver stand

Height together 5.8 cm, diameter of dish
6.9 cm, diameter of stand 8.1 cm
Naples Museum, inv. 110853 (dish) and
25549 (stand)
From Pompeii, found separately; 110853
was found 24 November 1875.

Little dishes of this sort were probably
used for serving hot sauces or (since the
form is found also in glass) small sweet-
meats.

315

Small fluted silver bowl

Height 5.1 cm, diameter 11.7 cm
Naples Museum, inv. 25553
From one of the sites in the Vesuvius area

Inverted conical bowls of this form, with
concave sides decorated with vertical
fluting and a scalloped rim, were common
in the first century A.D.
Strong 160.

316

Small fluted silver bowl

Height 5 cm, diameter 7.9 cm
Naples Museum, inv. 25557
From one of the sites in the Vesuvius area

A smaller version of No. 315. It lacks the
small rounded projections at the ends of
the flutes.

317

Silver spoon

Length 7.8 cm
Naples Museum, inv. 25413
From Herculaneum

The form of the handle is typical of
Roman spoons. This example has a simple
knop finial, and it is fastened to the bowl
by a "rat's tail" attachment. Spoons were
the only form of flatware normally used in
classical antiquity; forks were unknown,
and food was brought to the table in
ready-prepared portions, which did not
call for the use of a knife. Silver spoons
are common and are found in quite mod-
est households.
Strong 155-156.

318

Silver spoon

Length 14 cm
Naples Museum, inv. 25416
From one of the sites in the Vesuvius area

A larger version of No. 317, with a more
elaborately molded baluster knop.
Strong 155-156.

319

Silver egg cup

Height 8.4 cm
Naples Museum, inv. 116349
From House VIII, 2, 23

The little shallow cup on a short stem,
mounted on a large, lozenge-shaped base,
formed part of a service comprising four
ornate drinking cups, four smaller cups,
several little dishes like Nos. 313, 314,
four plates, four egg cups, and various
serving bowls.
Strong 154.

314

313

315

316

317   318

319

320
Two-handled silver drinking cup (cantharus)
Height 8.5 cm, diameter of bowl 12.5 cm
Naples Museum, inv. 25294
From one of the sites in the Vesuvius area

The bowl and the elaborately turned foot are plain except for a beaded border below the rim and a simple stamped motif on the foot. The handle mount terminates in a pair of birds' heads (see No. 323).

For similar cups, see Strong 133-134.

321
Silver plate
Diameter 17.7 cm, across the handles 22 cm
Naples Museum, inv. 25297
From one of the sites in the Vesuvius area

The plate is in the form of a shallow concave dish without a foot ring. The segmental handles, cast separately and soldered on, are decorated with a central palmette motif, flanked by foliage, ivy leaves, and the usual elongated birds' heads.

Strong 148f.

322
Silver jug
Height 12.5 cm, diameter of mouth 5.3 cm
Naples Museum, inv. 25692
From Pompeii

Tall, rounded shape with a plain, solid cast handle.

For the form, see Strong 140.

323
One-handled silver dipper, or skillet
Height 5.7 cm, diameter of lip 11.1 cm, length of handle 9 cm
Naples Museum, inv. 25344
From Pompeii

The bowl is plain. The handle, which was cast separately and attached to the bowl by means of two curving arms in the form of elongated birds' heads, is decorated in relief with a symmetrical foliate design terminating in a Dionysiac head with large ears, flanked by two ducks' heads (see No. 320). Vessels of this shape, usually found in pairs, had a long history, first appearing in the first century A.D. They are commonly found also in bronze, and they were most probably used for serving liquids, though not for the actual heating of them.

Strong 147-148.

324
Silver cup (calathus) decorated with sprigs of ivy and grape vines
Height 11.5 cm
Naples Museum, inv. 25300
From Pompeii

The foliage is rendered with a brilliantly varied use of the repoussé technique. In places the forms are merely sketched on the background, and in other areas they break into a high relief that seems almost completely free of the surface. The ivy and the grape vine, both plants sacred to Bacchus, god of wine and revelry, are observed with an extraordinary naturalism. The thinness of the leaf surface, the delicate veining, and even the growth rings where the stems have been cut through are all convincingly shown. The foliage densely covers the background and enriches the basic form of the cup. At Pompeii the *calathus* form appears frequently in glassware, like No. 95, as well as in silver. The foliage is worked in an outer case, while the moldings at the top are soldered onto a plain inner liner.

Ernst Künzl, "Der augusteische Silbercalathus im Rheinischen Landesmuseum Bonn" *BJb* 169 (1969) 329-331, note 15d; cf. A. Oliver, Jr., *Silver for the Gods* (Toledo 1977) 103, no. 60.

324

322

320

321

323

325

325
Silver cup (skyphos)
Height 8 cm
Naples Museum, inv. 145506
From the House of the Menander

This two-handled cup (*skyphos*), one of a pair, consists of a repoussé outer shell, a liner, and soldered-on base and handles. The decoration shows six deeds of Hercules in a vigorous, eclectic style. Details were originally picked out with gilding. The hero is alternately the beardless youth and the older man, bearded and muscle-bound. He brings in the Erymanthian Boar struggling on his shoulder, in the scheme known since Archaic times. He clubs at the head of a centaur, either his inebriated host Pholos or Nessus, ravisher of his wife, Deianira. He shoots down the vicious, buzzard-like Stymphalian Birds. On the other side Hercules makes an incongruously Parthenonic, horse-taming gesture at the tree with the golden apples of the Hesperides. The apples are guarded by a snake twining round the tree trunk, artistic prototype of the serpent in the Garden of Eden. The next adventure does involve horses, the man-eating mares of Diomedes, which trample a prostrate victim very like a fallen Lapith on one of the Parthenon metopes. Hercules subdues them in another, rarer horse-taming pose, early classical in origin. Finally, a rather sober, conventional, bearded Hercules leads in Cerberus, the three-headed watchdog of the underworld.

We know that Lysippos made a series of the Labors of Hercules for Alyzia, and that these were later brought to Rome. Attempts have been made to trace many Hellenistic or Roman versions back to these prototypes. The silversmith of the Hercules cups may have drawn on these as he certainly did on a variety of other sources.
Maiuri, *Menandro* 310-311, 314ff., no. 4, figs. 122-124, pls. XXVIII-XXX.

326
Silver cup (modiolus)
Height 8 cm
Naples Museum, inv. 145510
From the House of the Menander

This is one of a pair of mug-shaped silver cups, made up, as was customary for such vessels, of an outer shell worked in repoussé, a smooth inner cup, a cast, soldered-on handle. Winged Cupids and Victories, destined, obviously, to beat them, drive paired horses in the dangerous ancient sport of chariot racing. Navigation was even more crucial than speed, and maneuvers to make one's opponents crash on the tight curves of the elongated oval track were an important part of the charioteer's skill. One of the Cupids has already come to grief. He sprawls on the ground, his horses rearing and shying in their tangled harness. In the background are the monuments of the *spina*, the central island of the racecourse. Two columns support a row of eggs and dolphins; these were moved to indicate which lap of the race was being run. Cupids earnestly engaged in adult activities are familiar from Pompeian painting; the conceit is Hellenistic in origin. Their mock-serious chariot race appears on Roman sarcophagi, for which the House of the Menander cups are an interesting antecedent.
Maiuri, *Menandro* 343ff., no. 11, fig. 134 and pls. XLI-XLIV.

326

327 (not illus.)
Reproduction of one of the painted Second Style walls from the newly excavated villa at Oplontis
Length 8.80 m, height 5.60 m
Lent by Imperial Tobacco Limited
Reproduced by courtesy of the excavator, Professor Alfonso De Franciscis

The building to which this painting belongs was part of an opulent seaside villa (*villa marittima*) about three miles west of Pompeii, in the modern Torre Annunziata. The eruption buried it beneath nearly two meters of ash and pumice, then five meters of volcanic mud, and although the site has been known for a long time and was the subject of desultory exploration in 1839-40, it was not until 1964 that systematic excavations were put in hand by Professor De Franciscis.

The remains at present exposed comprise the greater part of the main residential block, together with its domestic service quarters, and to the east of it (not shown on the plan) part of an extensive *villa rustica* annex. On the north side the main block backed onto a garden. The south façade opened onto a terraced platform, which in antiquity probably fronted directly onto the sea. Viewed from the sea or from the garden behind, the residential block would have been roughly symmetrical about a line of large rooms running north and south, comprising a projecting atrium complex at the south end and, at the north end, beyond a small internal garden courtyard (Room 20), a large *oecus* (Room 21) opening onto the garden between the columns of a gabled porch. These rooms and those to the west of them constituted the main residence. To the east, screened from the main façade by a row of smaller rooms, were more utilitarian rooms grouped around an inner peristyle. These included the quarters of the domestic staff. Along the south frontage, following the outline of the plan, ran a continuous portico, such as one sees in the wall paintings of *villae marittimae* (e.g., No. 1).

At the time of the eruption only the servants' wing was occupied. The main residence, stripped of its furnishings, was awaiting modernization and redecoration. Another few years, perhaps months, and the magnificent series of Second Style paintings that are its especial glory would probably have gone the way of the paintings in the large garden *oecus* (Room 21), the walls of which were found already stripped bare. As it is, five rooms retain their original Second Style decoration: the atrium (5); a bed-chamber (11) and a day-room (23) on either side of it; a *triclinium* dining room (14), which adjoins the unusually large and well-appointed kitchen (7); and the large hall (15), which occupied the middle of the south front of the west wing.

No. 327, which covered the whole of the east wall in Room 15, still retains the formal simplicity of the early Second Style schemes, viewed as if through a simple colonnade of lofty Corinthian columns set on a low plinth projecting from the wall behind. But above eye-level the solid wall has been almost entirely eliminated, surviving only as an iconostasis-like screen, with two horizontal architraves and a central arch, which partition up the receding architectural vistas portrayed beyond them. In the two lateral bays a pair of monumental double colonnades frame the central motif, a Delphic tripod, shown upraised on a tall, slender, circular pedestal and viewed as if through an open gateway leading into a garden. One notes the theatrical masks displayed on brackets; the *pinakes* in their wooden frames perched above the outer ends of the screen; the clever contrast of color between the upper and the lower colonnades; and in the two narrow outer bays the friezes of shields, a motif repeated both in the atrium and in Room 23. The perspective is not the strict, single-viewpoint perspective of Renaissance and modern practice, but it is a remarkably sophisticated piece of visual illusionism. Painted around 40 B.C. it is one of the surviving masterpieces of the fully developed Second Style.

Parts of the building were subsequently modernized a generation or so later. To this time belong the fine early Third Style paintings in the bath suite, perhaps also those of the *cubiculum* in the west wing (Room 38), which still retains its exquisitely painted red ceiling. The north façade in its present form may also be of this period. To the final phase before A.D. 79 belongs the highly simplified decoration of the inner peristyle of the east wing.

To whom did this villa belong, and can we give it a name? As regards ownership, there is some evidence that its last occupant was the wife of Nero, Poppaea Sabina, who died in A.D. 65. The Poppaei were a well-known Pompeian family, and it is an established fact that Poppaea Sabina, while empress, owned property within the territory of the city. Her death, followed in 68 by that of Nero, would help to explain why the property, though in good condition and destined for restoration, was still unoccupied in A.D. 79.

As for the name, Oplontis (or Eplontis), this is found only in two late itineraries and on the Roman map known as the Peutinger Table, where it is marked as a road station between Herculaneum and Pompeii. This may be a survival from pre-eruption times (such documents are notoriously conservative) or denote a later settlement. There are many records of classical finds in Torre Annunziata, in at least one instance coming from what was evidently another luxury villa. The "Oplontis" villa is a vivid reminder of how much may still await discovery.

GLOSSARY

Acroterion (plural *acroteria*) Decorative finial at the apex or the outer angles of a gabled roof.

Aedicula A small ornamental structure projecting from a wall, usually consisting of a gable carried by a pair of colonnettes or pilasters. Often reproduced in the fantasy architecture of Pompeian wall paintings.

Aedile (Latin *aedilis*) One of the pair of junior magistrates elected annually to supervise the day-to-day administration of the city. The office already existed in Samnite Pompeii.

Ala A wing extending to right and left at the far end of the atrium of a typical Pompeian house, giving access to the rooms on either side of the *tablinum*.

Amorino A cupid.

Aphrodite, see *Venus*.

Apollo The Greek god of the arts and music, early absorbed into the Italian pantheon. The principal divinity of Samnite Pompeii.

Artemis The Roman Diana, commonly portrayed as a huntress in her role as the goddess of forests and hills and of wild creatures.

Athena, see *Minerva*.

Atrium The central hall of a traditional Italic house. The roof normally sloped inward to a rectangular central opening.

Bacchus, see *Dionysus*.

Basilica A colonnaded public hall, usually adjoining the forum, used for commercial and judicial business.

Belvedere A raised building from which to enjoy a view.

Caduceus The wand carried by Hermes (Mercury), with wings and two symmetrically entwined serpents.

Cornucopia A horn overflowing with fruits, symbol of plenty.

Cubiculum (plural *cubicula*) Bedroom.

Dionysus The Roman Bacchus, god of wine and of the theater, whose cult involved "mysteries" as well as ecstatic rites. Among his followers were satyrs, sileni, and maenads. Satyrs, originally spirits of wild life in the woods and hills, in Roman times were regularly portrayed in youthful human form but with pointed ears and tails and frequently with some of the goat-like attributes of the god Pan. Sileni, like satyrs, were originally woodland creatures part-man, part-horse, normally shown as elderly, shaggy, paunchy figures, frequently the worse for wine. Maenads were their female companions, usually portrayed in attitudes of ecstatic abandon.

Duovir (plural *duoviri*) One of the pair of senior magistrates elected annually to represent the city and to act as joint chairmen of the city council. Every fifth year these magistrates had special powers and were called *duoviri quinquennales*. The equivalent magistrates in the Samnite period were called *meddices* (singular *meddix*).

Emblema Strictly, a small panel in fine mosaic, produced separately to be inserted into a larger floor (see No. 61). Also used as the central feature of any larger decorative design.

Ephebe (Greek *ephebos*) An aristocratic Greek youth who had not yet completed his education.

Escutcheon Term used to indicate a piece of applied decoration, as commonly in metalwork.

Exedra A large rectangular or curved recess opening off a room or corridor.

Hera, see *Juno*.

Hercules Latin form of Heracles, the Greek hero who performed twelve labors for the king of Argos and was later worshiped as a god for his strength and power to repel evil. Particularly favored by merchants.

Herm The name derives from early Greek representations of the god Hermes in the form of a rectangular shaft with a carved head. Later, more elaborate versions carried heads also of other divinities and human portraits.

Hermes The Roman Mercury, the messenger of the gods and patron divinity of commerce.

Impluvium The rectangular basin in the center of the atrium of a Pompeian house, situated beneath the rectangular opening *(compluvium)* in the center of the roof.

Insula (Latin, "island") Term used conventionally to denote an ancient city block.

Intarsia (Italian *intarsio*) Shaped designs of wood, stone, or metal inlaid into a background that has been cut out to receive them. See Nos. 174-176.

Juno The Greek Hera, the consort of Jupiter and the goddess specially concerned with those aspects of life which affected women (the home, marriage, childbirth, etc.).

Jupiter God of the heavens, whose special attribute was a thunderbolt. The patron divinity of Rome (Jupiter Optimus Maximus Capitolinus) and, with Juno and Minerva, the senior member of the Capitoline triad. Generally equated with the Greek Zeus.

Lararium Household shrine, with statuettes or painted representations of the Lares, the traditional guardians of the house, and of other favored gods. See No. 210.

Lares, see *Lararium*.

Maenad, see under *Dionysus*.

Medusa A mythical female monster with snakes for hair and eyes that turned to stone those who looked upon her.

Mercury, see *Hermes*.

Minerva Goddess of wisdom, learning, and the arts and sciences. With Jupiter and Juno, the third member of the Roman Capitoline triad. Equated by the Romans with Athena.

Oecus (Greek *oikos*) A richly decorated living room.

Onkos Greek hairstyle, found commonly on theatrical masks; see Nos. 306-309.

Opus sectile Paving or wall decoration made of interlocking shaped pieces of colored marble.

Oscillum (plural *oscilla*) Originally a mask or other ritual object, hung from a sacred tree, which "oscillated" or spun in the wind. Later used in a variety of shapes in peristyle gardens, hung from the architrave between the columns.

Ovolo (from the Latin *ovum*, an egg) A convex molding of egg-shaped profile.

Palaestra Open space reserved for exercise and sport. Usually enclosed by colonnades.

Pan A Greek pastoral divinity, responsible for the fertility of flocks. Often shown as half-goat, half-man, playing on his panpipe (see Nos. 69, 114).

Peristyle The inner, colonnaded garden court of a Pompeian (or Hellenistic) house, around which the main living rooms of the later houses were grouped.

Pinax (plural *pinakes*) A panel picture painted on wood or marble and often enclosed in a frame that could be closed like a triptych. Few actual *pinakes* have survived, but there are many representations of them in wall paintings.

Priapus Rustic god of fertility, regularly portrayed displaying a huge male organ.

Satyr, see under *Dionysus*.

Silenus, see under *Dionysus*.

Siren A mythological creature, half-woman and half-bird.

Stucco A hard slow-setting plaster based on lime, used for rendering wall surfaces or for molded architectural detail.

Tablinum The central room at the far end of an atrium house, often with a window opening onto the garden beyond. It was the main reception room and could be closed off from the atrium by a screen or curtains. In the late houses it opens also onto the peristyle.

Tempietto (Italian) A small temple-shaped building, either circular or gabled, with columns.

Terra sigillata Conventional name for the red-gloss pottery first produced in Italy at Arezzo, and later in many other places both in Italy and the western provinces of the Empire. It is found both in plain forms and with molded relief decoration, in both cases closely modeled on the shapes and ornament of silverware. See Nos. 258-262.

Tesserae (*tessellae*) Small cubes or splinters of colored stone, glass, or paste used to make mosaics.

Tholos A circular columned pavilion or *tempietto*.

Thyrsus A long staff, tipped with a pine cone or with bunches of ivy or vine leaves, carried by Dionysus or his followers.

Travertine Silvery-gray calcareous stone extensively used in the area around Rome, occasionally elsewhere. Most references to "travertine" at Pompeii refer in fact to the gray limestone of the nearby hills.

Triclinium The dining room of a Roman house or its open-air equivalent. See page 95.

Tufa (Italian *tufo*) A rock formed of hardened volcanic ash, easily worked when freshly quarried.

Uraeus Egyptian cobra sacred to Isis.

Venus The Greek Aphrodite, goddess of love and patron goddess of Pompeii.

Volute A spiral scroll, as on an Ionic capital.

Zeus The senior member of the Greek Olympian pantheon, in many aspects to be equated with the Roman Jupiter.

BIBLIOGRAPHY

1. Periodicals and reference works cited in the catalogue in abbreviated form

AA — *Archaeologischer Anzeiger* (in *JdAI*), Berlin.

AJA — *American Journal of Archaeology*, New York.

Annali dell'Inst — *Annali dell'Instituto di Corrispondenza Archeologica*, Rome.

AZ — *Archäologische Zeitung*, Berlin.

BdA — *Bollettino d'Arte*, Florence.

BJb — *Bonner Jahrbücher*, Bonn.

BMC Gems — H. B. Walters, *Catalogue of the Engraved Gems and Cameos . . . in the British Museum*, 2nd ed., London 1926.

BMC Lamps — H. B. Walters, *Catalogue of the Greek and Roman Lamps . . . in the British Museum*, London 1914.

BMFA — *Bulletin of the Museum of Fine Arts, Boston*.

Bronzi di Ercolano — *Le Antichità di Ercolano esposte*, vols V-VI (= I *Bronzi di Ercolano* 1-2), Naples 1767 and 1771.

Bull Inst — *Bullettino dell'Instituto di Corrispondenza Archeologica*, Rome.

Ceci — Museo Nazionale, Naples, *Piccoli bronzi del Real Museo borbonico . . . descritte e disegnata da Carlo Ceci*, 2nd ed., Naples 1858.

CIL — *Corpus Inscriptionum Latinarum*.

Daremberg & Saglio — C. Daremberg and E. Saglio, *Dictionnaire des antiquités grecques et romaines*, Paris 1877-1919.

EAA — *Enciclopedia dell' arte antica, classica e orientale*, vols I-VII, Rome 1958-1966.

ILS — H. Dessau, ed., *Inscriptiones Latinae Selectae*, 3 vols, Berlin 1892-1916.

JdAI — *Jahrbuch des deutschen archaeologischen Instituts*, Berlin.

JRS — *Journal of Roman Studies*, London.

Kraus & von Matt — T. Kraus and L. von Matt, *Pompeii and Herculaneum: Living Cities of the Dead*, New York 1975 (English translation of *Lebendiges Pompeji*, Cologne 1973).

MAAR — *Memoirs of the American Academy in Rome*, Rome.

MB — *Real Museo Borbonico*, 1st ed. in 16 vols, Naples 1824-1857; subsequent ed. with major alterations, in 9 vols, Rome 1837-1845.

MdI — *Mitteilungen des deutschen archäologischen Instituts* (1948), Berlin.

MemErc — *Memorie della Regale Accademia Ercolanese di Archeologia*, Naples 1840-1848.

MemLinc — *Memorie dell'Accademia nazionale dei Lincei*, Rome.

Mon Pitt — *Monumenti della pittura antica scoperti in Italia*, Rome.

Muse — *Muse, Annual of the Museum of Art and Archaeology*, University of Missouri-Columbia.

Neue Forschungen — *Neue Forschungen in Pompeji*, ed. B. Andreae and H. Kyrieleis, Recklinghausen 1975.

NSc — *Notizie degli scavi di antichità communicate alla (Reale) Accademia dei Lincei*, Rome.

PAH — *Pompeianorum Antiquitatum Historia*, ed. G. Fiorelli, 3 vols, Naples 1860-1864.

Pitture di Ercolano — *Le Antichità di Ercolano esposte*, vols I-V (= *Le Pitture di Ercolano*, 1-5), Naples 1757-1779.

Pompeiana — *Pompeiana. Raccolta di studi per il secondo centenario degli scavi di Pompei*, Naples 1950.

RAAN (Rend Nap) — *Rendiconti dell'Accademia di Archeologia, Lettere e Belle Arti di Napoli*.

RendLinc — *Rendiconti della R. Accademia dei Lincei*.

Rev Arch — *Revue Archéologique*, Paris.

RM — *Mitteilungen des deutschen archäologischen Instituts. Römische Abteilung*, Rome (commonly referred to as *Römische Mitteilungen*).

2. General bibliography, listed in alphabetical order under author's name. Any abbreviations used in the catalogue are given below in parentheses following the individual entries.

Andreae, B. "Rekonstruktion der grossen Oecus der Villa des P. Fannius Synistor in Boscoreale," in *Neue Forschungen* 71-92.

Andreae, B., and others. *Pompeji: Leben und Kunst in den Vesuvstädten* [catalogue of exhibition Villa Hügel Essen]. Recklinghausen 1975 (Andreae, *Pompeji*).

Andreau, J. *Les affaires de Monsieur Jucundus*. Ecole Française de Rome, 1974 (Andreau).

Augusti, S. "La technica dell'antica pittura parietale pompeiana." *Pompeiana* 1950, 313-354.

Barnabei, F. *La Villa Pompeiana di P. Fannio Sinistore scoperta presso Boscoreale*. Rome 1901.

Barnabei, F. *Pompei e la regione sotterrata dal Vesuvio nell'anno LXXIX*. Naples 1879.

Beloch, J. *Campanien im Alterthum*. 2nd ed. Naples 1890.

Beyen, H. G. *Über Stilleben aus Pompeji und Herculaneum*. The Hague 1928 (Beyen, *Stilleben*).

Beyen, H. G. "The Workshops of the 'Fourth Style' at Pompeii and in Its Neighbourhood." 1. *Studia archaeologica G. Van Hoorn oblato*. Leiden 1951.

Bianchi Bandinelli, R. *Rome: The Centre of Power. Roman Art to A.D. 200*. London 1970 (Bianchi Bandinelli).

Bieber, M. *History of the Greek and Roman Theater*. Princeton 1939 (Bieber, *Theater*).

Blanckenhagen, P. H. von, and Alexander, M. *The Paintings from Boscotrecase*. Heidelberg 1962 (Blanckenhagen and Alexander, *Boscotrecase*).

Boyce, G. K. "Corpus of the Lararia of Pompeii," *MAAR* XIV, 1937 (Boyce).

Breglia, L. *Catalogo delle oreficerie del Museo di Napoli*. Rome 1941 (Breglia).

Carrington, R. C. *Pompeii*. Oxford 1936.

Carrington, R. C. "Studies in the Campanian 'Villa rusticae'." *JRS* 21 (1931), 110-130.

Casella, D. "Frutta nelle pitture pompeiane." *Pompeiana* 1950, 355-386.

Castrén, P. *Ordo Populusque Pompeianus: Polity and Society in Roman Pompeii* (Acta Instituti Romani Finlandiae vol. VIII). Rome 1975 (Castrén).

Chiurazzi, Società anonima, fonderie-ceramica-marmeria, Napoli. *Catalogo*, compilato da Salvatore Chiurazzi. Naples, n.d. (Chiurazzi).

Coarelli, F., ed. *Guida archeologica di Pompei*. Verona 1976.

Comparetti, D., and De Petra, G. *La Villa Ercolanese dei Pisoni, suoi monumenti e biblioteca.* Turin 1883.

Cosenza, G. *Stabia: Memorie storiche ed archeologiche.* Castellamare di Stabia 1890.

Cosenza, G. *Studi archeologici topografici e storici su Stabia.* Trani 1907.

Croisille, J. M. *Les natures mortes campaniennes* (Coll. Latomus, LXXVI). Brussels 1965 (Croisille).

Curtius, L. *Die Wandmalerei Pompejis.* Leipzig 1929; reprinted Darmstadt 1972 (Curtius).

D'Arms, J. H. *Romans on the Bay of Naples.* Cambridge, Mass. 1970 (D'Arms).

Dawson, Ch. M. "Romano-Campanian Mythological Landscape Painting." *Yale Classical Studies* 9, 1944 (Dawson).

De Franciscis, A. *The Pompeian Wall Paintings in the Roman Villa of Oplontis.* Recklinghausen 1975.

De Franciscis, A. *Il ritratto romano a Pompei.* Naples 1951 (De Franciscis).

Della Corte, M. *Case ed abitanti di Pompei.* Pompei Scavi 1954.

Della Corte, M. *Pompei: I nuovi scavi e l'anfiteatro.* Pompeii 1930.

De Ridder, A. *Les bronzes antiques du Louvre* II, *Les Instruments.* Paris 1915.

Di Capua, F. "Sacrari Pompeiani." *Pompeiana* 1950, 60-85.

D'Orsi, L. *Come ritrovai l'Antica Stabia.* Milan 1962.

Elia, O. "Nota per uno studio della decorazione parietale a Pompei." *Pompeiana* 1950, 97-110.

Elia, O. "Le pitture della casa del Citarista." *MonPitt: Pompei,* fasc. 1, Rome 1937.

Elia, O. "Le pitture del Tempio di Iside." *MonPitt: Pompei,* fasc. 3-4. Rome 1942 (Elia, *MonPitt*).

Elia, O. *Le pitture di Stabia.* Naples 1957.

Elia, O. *Pitture murali e mosaici del Museo Nazionale di Napoli.* Naples 1932 (Elia).

Eschebach, H. "Feststellung unter der Oberfläche des Jahres 79 n. Chr. im Bereich der Insula VII, 1 — Stabianer Thermen — in Pompeii" in *Neue Forschungen* 179-190.

Eschebach, H. "Die stadtbauliche Entwicklung des antiken Pompeji." *RM* Ergänzungsheft no. 17. Heidelberg 1970.

Etienne, R. *La vie quotidienne à Pompei.* Paris 1966.

Fienga, F. "Esplorazione del pago marittimo pompeiano." *Atti del III Congresso Nazionale di Studi Romani.* Bologna 1934, 172-176.

Fiorelli, G. *Catalogo del Museo Nazionale di Napoli, Armi antiche.* Naples 1869 (Fiorelli, *Armi antiche*).

Fiorelli, G. *Catalogo del Museo Nazionale di Napoli, Raccolta pornografica.* Naples 1866 (Fiorelli, *Raccolta pornografica*).

Fiorelli, G. *Gli scavi di Pompei dal 1861 al 1872.* Naples 1873 (Fiorelli, *Scavi*).

Gell, W., and Gandi, J. P., *Pompeiana: The Topography, Edifices and Ornaments of Pompeii.* 2 vols. London 1817-1819.

Gigante, M. "La cultura letteraria a Pompei." *Pompeiana* 1950, 111-143.

Gusman, P. *Pompéi: La ville, les moeurs, les arts.* Paris [1899?]; English ed. *Pompeii: The City, Its Life and Art.* London 1900 (Gusman).

Harden, D. B. "The Glass," in Hawkes, C. F. C., and Hull, M. R. *Camulodunum,* 287-306. Oxford 1947 (Harden, *Camulodunum*).

Helbig, W. *Untersuchungen über die campanische Wandmalerei.* Leipzig 1873.

Helbig, W. *Wandgemälde der vom Vesuv verschutteten Städte.* Leipzig 1868 (Helbig).

Héron de Villefosse, V. "Le Trésor de Boscoreale." *Monuments Piot* V, 1899.

Higgins, R. A. *Greek and Roman Jewellery.* London 1961.

Ippel, A. *Der dritte pompejanische Stil.* Berlin 1910.

Isings, C. *Roman Glass from Dated Finds* (Archaeologica traiectina II). Groningen 1957 (Isings).

Jacono, L. "Note di archeologia marittima. 1. Il Porto di Pompei?." *Neapolis* I, 1913 fasc. III-IV, 353ff.

Jashemsky, W. F. "The Caupona of Euxinus at Pompeii." *Archaeology* XX (1967) 36-44.

Jashemsky, W. F. "The Discovery of a Market Garden Orchard at Pompeii." *AJA* 78 (1974) 391-404.

Jashemsky, W. F. "Excavation in the Foro Boario at Pompeii." *AJA* 72 (1968) 69-73.

Jashemsky, W. F. "From Vesuvius' Dust: Pompeii Emerges a City of Gardens, Vineyards." *Landscape Architecture,* May 1976, 224-230.

Jashemsky, W. F. "A Large Vineyard Discovered in Ancient Pompeii." *Science* 180 (1973) 826.

Jashemsky, W. F. "Pompeian Gardens Yield Their Secrets." *American Horticultural Magazine,* spring 1970, 54-63.

Jashemsky, W. F. "Tomb Gardens at Pompeii." *Classical Journal* 66 (1970-71) 97-115.

Johannowsky, W. "Contributi alla topografia della Campania antica." *RAAN* n.s. XXVII 1952, 83-146.

Kapossy, B. *Brunnenfiguren der hellenistischen und römischen Zeit.* Zurich 1969 (Kapossy, *Brunnenfiguren*).

Kirschen, F. *Die Stadtmauern von Pompeji* (Die hellenistische Kunst in Pompeji VII). Berlin 1941.

Kluge, K., and Lehmann-Hartleben, K. *Die antiken Grossbronzen.* 3 vols. Berlin and Leipzig 1927 (Kluge-Hartleben).

Laidlaw, A. "A Reconstruction of the First Style Decoration in the Alexander Exedra of the House of the Faun," in *Neue Forschungen* 39-52.

Lauter, H. "Zur Siedlungsstruktur Pompejis in Samnitischen Zeit," in *Neue Forschungen* 147-154.

Lauter-Bufe, H. "Zur architektonischen Gartengestaltung in Pompeji und Herculaneum," in *Neue Forschungen* 169-173.

Lehmann, P. W. *Roman Wall Paintings from Boscoreale in the Metropolitan Museum of Art.* Cambridge, Mass. 1953.

Lepore, E. "Orientamenti per la storia sociale di Pompei." *Pompeiana* 1950, 144-166.

Levi, A. *Le terracotte figurati del Museo Nazionale di Napoli.* Florence 1926 (Levi).

Maiuri, A. *La casa del Menandro e il suo tesoro di argenteria.* 2 vols. Rome 1933 (Maiuri, *Menandro*).

Maiuri, A. *Ercolano: i nuovi scavi (1927-1958),* vol. I. Rome 1958 (Maiuri, *Ercolano*).

Maiuri, A. "Geologia ed archeologia ad Ercolano ed a Pompei." *RAAN* n.s. XXII 1942-1946, 113-140.

Maiuri, A. "Gli scavi di Pompei dal 1879 al 1948." *Pompeiana* 1950, 9-40.

Maiuri, A. *Herculaneum.* Paris 1932.

Maiuri, A. "Le pitture delle case di M. Fabius Amandio, del Sacerdos Amandus, di Cornelius Teges." *MonPitt: Pompei,* fasc. 2, Rome 1938.

Maiuri, A. *L'ultima fase edilizia di Pompei.* Rome 1942 (Maiuri, *L'ultima fase*).

Maiuri, A. *La Villa dei Misteri.* Rome 1947.

Mau, A. *Geschichte der decorativen Wandmalerei in Pompeji.* Berlin 1882.

Mau, A. *Pompeji in Leben und Kunst.* 2nd ed. Leipzig 1908; supplement to 2nd ed., Leipzig 1913.

Mau, A., and Kelsey, F. W. *Pompeii, Its Life and Art.* New York 1899 (Mau-Kelsey).

Mustilli, D. "Botteghe di scultori, marmorarii, bronzieri e caelatores in Pompei." *Pompeiana* 1950, 206-229.

Mustilli, D. "La villa pseudo-urbana ercolanese." *RAAN* n.s. XXXI 1956, 77-97.

Niccolini, F. *Le case ed i monumenti di Pompei designati e descritti.* Naples 1854-96 (Niccolini).

Nissen, H. *Pompeianische Studien zur Städtekunde des Altertums.* Leipzig 1877.

Noack, F., and Lehmann-Hartleben, K. *Baugeschichtliche Untersuchungen am Stadtrand von Pompeji* (Denkmäler antiker Architektur II). Berlin and Leipzig 1936.

Onorato, G. O. "La data del terremoto di Pompei: 5 febbraio 62 d.C." *RAAN* ser.8, IV 1949, 644-661.

Overbeck, J. *Pompeji in seinem Gebäuden, Alterthümern und Kunstwerken.* Leipzig 1884.

Packer, J. "Middle and Lower Class Housing in Pompeii and Herculaneum: A Preliminary Survey," in *Neue Forschungen* 133-146.

Palombi, A. "La fauna marina nei mosaici e nei dipinti pompeiani." *Pompeiana* 1950, 425-455.

Pernice, E. *Gefässe und Geräte aus Bronze* (Die hellenistische Kunst in Pompeji IV). Berlin 1925 (Pernice IV).

Pernice, E. *Hellenistische Tische, Zisternenmundungen, Beckenuntersätze, Altare, und Truhen* (Die hellenistische Kunst in Pompeji V). Berlin 1932 (Pernice V).

Pernice, E. *Pavimente und figürliche Mosaiken* (Die hellenistische Kunst in Pompeji VI). Berlin 1938 (Pernice VI).

Peters, W. J. T. *Landscape in Romano-Campanian Mural Painting.* Assen 1963 (Peters).

Presuhn, E. *Pompeii: Les dernières fouilles de 1874-1878.* Leipzig 1878.

Pugliese Carratelli, G. "L'instrumentum scriptorium nei monumenti pompeiani ed ercolanensi." *Pompeiana* 1950, 266-278.

Reuterswaard, P. *Studien zur Polychromie der Plastik: Griechenland und Rom.* Stockholm 1960 (Reuterswaard, *Polychromie*).

Richardson, L. "Pompeii: The Casa dei Dioscuri and Its Painters." *MAAR* XXIII, 1955 (Richardson).

Rittmann, A. "L'eruzione vesuviana del 79." *Pompeiana* 1950, 456-474.

Rizzo, G. E. *La pittura ellenistica-romana.* Milan 1929.

Rocco, A. "*Pompeiana supelex.*" *Pompeiana* 1950, 278-287.

Rodenwaldt, G. *Die Komposition der pompejanische Wandgemälde.* Berlin 1900.

Rostowzew, M. "Die hellenistische-römische Architekturlandschaft." *RM* XXVI (1911) 1-186 (Rostowzew, "Architekturlandschaft").

Roux Ainé, H. *Herculanum et Pompei: Recueil général des peintures, bronzes, mosaiques, etc.* 8 vols. Paris 1870-1872.

Ruesch, A., ed. *Guida illustrata del Museo Nazionale di Napoli.* Naples 1908 (Ruesch).

Ruggiero, M. *Degli scavi di Stabia dal 1749 al 1782.* Naples 1881 (Ruggiero, *Stabia*).

Salmon, E. T. *Samnium and the Samnites.* Cambridge 1967.

Schefold, K. *La peinture pompéienne* (Coll. Latomus no. CVIII). Brussels 1972 (Schefold).

Schefold, K. *Pompejanische Malerei.* Basle 1952.

Schefold, K. *Vergessenes Pompeji.* Munich 1962.

Schefold, K. *Die Wände Pompejis.* Berlin 1957 (Schefold, *WP*).

Siviero, R. *Gli ori e le ambre del Museo Nazionale di Napoli.* Florence 1954 (Siviero).

Sogliano, A. "Le pitture murale campagne scoverte negli anni 1867-1879 descritte," in *Pompei e la regione sotterrata dal Vesuvio*, vol. 11 87 ff. Naples 1879 (Sogliano).

Sogliano, A. *Pompei nel suo sviluppo storico. Pompei preromana (dalle origini alle 80 av. C.).* Rome 1937.

Spano, G. "Porte e regione pompeiane e vie campane." *RAAN* n.s. XVII, 1937, 269ff.

Spinazzola, V. *Le arti decorative in Pompei e nel Museo Nazionale di Napoli.* Milan 1928 (Spinazzola).

Spinazzola, V. *Pompei alla luce degli scavi nuovi di Via dell' Abbondanza*, vols. I-III. Rome 1953 (Spinazzola-Aurigemma).

Strong, D. E. *Greek and Roman Silver Plate.* London 1966 (Strong).

Tanzer, H. H. *The Common People of Pompeii* (The Johns Hopkins University Studies in Archaeology no. 29). Baltimore 1939.

Thédenat, H. *Les villes d'art célèbres: Pompéi.* Paris 1910.

Tran tam Tinh, V. *Le culte des divinités orientales à Herculaneum* (Etudes préliminaires aux réligions orientales dans l'empire romain no. 17). Leiden 1971 (Tran tam Tinh, *Herculaneum*).

Tran tam Tinh, V. *Essai sur le culte d'Isis à Pompéi.* Paris 1964 (Tran tam Tinh, *Pompéi*).

Tran tam Tinh, V. "Les problèmes du culte de Cybèle et d'Attis à Pompéi," in *Neue Forschungen* 279-283 (Tran tam Tinh, 1975).

Van Buren, A. W. *A Companion to the Study of Pompeii and Herculaneum.* Rome 1933; 2nd ed. Rome 1938.

Venuti, M. *A Description of the Discovery of the Ancient City of Heraclea*, trs. W. Skurray. London 1750 (Venuti, *Heraclea*).

Von Rohden, H. *Die Terracotten von Pompeji.* Stuttgart 1880 (Von Rohden).

Waldstein, C., and Shoobridge, L. *Herculaneum Past, Present and Future.* London 1908.

Webster, T. B. L. *Monuments Illustrating New Comedy.* 2nd ed. (University of London, Bulletin of the Institute of Classical Studies, Supplement 24, 1969) (Webster, *New Comedy*).

Webster, T. B. L. *Monuments Illustrating Tragedy and Satyr Play.* 2nd ed. (University of London, Bulletin of the Institute of Classical Studies, Supplement 20, 1967) (Webster, *Tragedy and Satyr Play*).

Winter, F. *Die figürlichen Typen der Terracotten.* 2 vols. Leipzig 1903 (Winter).

Witt, R. E. *Isis in the Graeco-Roman World.* London 1971.

Zahn, W. *Die schönsten Ornamente und merkwürdigsten Gemälde aus Pompeji, Herkulanum und Stabiae.* 3 vols. Berlin 1827-1859.

Zevi, F. *La casa Reg. IX, 5, 18-21 a Pompei e le sue pitture.* Rome 1964.

3. Some Recent Books in English

Boethius, A., and Ward-Perkins, J. B. *Etruscan and Roman Architecture*, chs. 13 and 14 (Pelican History of Art). London 1970.

Brion, M. *Pompeii and Herculaneum: The Glory and the Grief.* London and Toronto 1960.

Bulwer-Lytton, E. *The Last Days of Pompeii*, abridged ed. London 1976.

Clay, E., and Frederiksen, M. *Sir William Gell in Italy: Letters to the Society of Dilettanti, 1831-1835.* London 1976.

Deiss, J. J. *Herculaneum, Italy's Buried Treasure.* New York 1966.

Grant, M. *Cities of Vesuvius: Pompeii and Herculaneum.* London 1971 (Grant, *Cities of Vesuvius*).

Grant, M., De Simone, A., and Merella, M. T. *Erotic Art in Pompeii.* London 1975 (Grant, De Simone, and Merella).

Leppmann, W. *Pompeii in Fact and Fiction.* London 1968.

McKay, A. G. *Houses, Villas and Palaces in the Roman World*, ch. 2. London 1975.

Trevelyan, R. *The Shadow of Vesuvius: Pompeii AD 79.* London 1976.